Other titles in the *Hospital Medicine* monograph series:

Clinical Governance: One year on edited by Alastair P Scotland

Health Services Research: Avoiding common pitfalls edited by Huw TO Davies

A Guide to Medical Publishing and Writing

Hospital Medicine monograph

**edited by
Peter Richardson**

Quay Books

Mark Allen Publishing Ltd

Quay Books Division, Mark Allen Publishing Limited,Jesses Farm, Snow Hill, Dinton, Wiltshire, SP3 5HN

British Library Cataloguing-in-Publication Data
A catalogue record is available for this book

© Mark Allen Publishing Ltd 2002
ISBN 1 85642 222 4

Printed in the UK by Cromwell Press, Trowbridge, Wiltshire

Contents

Contributors

Professor GCJ Bennett is Professor, Academic Department of Health Care of Older People, The Royal London Hospital, London E1 4DG.

Dr Carol Cooper is a GP, freelance writer and medical adviser to the *Sun* newspaper.

Professor Huw TO Davies is Professor of Health Care Policy and Management in the Department of Management, University of St Andrews, St Katherine's West, St Andrews, Fife KY16 9AL.

Dr Neville W Goodman is Consultant Anaesthetist, Southmead Hospital, Bristol BS10 5NB.

Mr Robert Kiley is Head of Systems Strategy, the Wellcome Library for the History and Understanding of Medicine, Wellcome Trust, London NW1 2BE and joint author of the *Patient's Internet Handbook* (RSM Press, 2002).

Mr Roger S Kirby is Consultant Urologist, St George's Hospital, London SW17 0QT.

Ms Rebecca Linssen is Editor of *Hospital Medicine*, Mark Allen Pubishing Limited, Croxted Mews, 286A–288 Croxted Road, London SE24 9BY.

Dr Sheila McKenzie is Consultant Paediatrician, Barts and Royal London NHS Trust, Whitechapel Road, London E1 1BB.

Ms Sally Morris is Secretary-General, Association of Learned and Professional Society Publishers, Morris Associates, South House, The Street, Clapham, Worthing, West Sussex BN13 3UU.

Mr Geoffrey Nuttall is Managing Director of Greenwich Medical Media Ltd, 137 Euston Road, London NW1 2AA.

Dr Elisabeth Paice is Dean Director, Thames Postgraduate Medical and Dental Education, 33 Millman Street, London WC1N 3EJ.

Mr Peter Richardson is Managing Director, The Royal Society of Medicine Press, London W1G 0AE.

Professor Robin CN Williamson is Consultant Surgeon in the Department of Surgery, Hammersmith Hospital, London W12 ONN and Associate Dean of the Royal Society of Medicine.

Ms Mira Vogel is Research Fellow, Academic Department of Health Care of Older People, The Royal London Hospital, London E1 4DG.

Preface

Writing and publishing are an integral part of any healthcare practitioner's training, alongside their work with patients. This book contains a collection of articles for health practitioners, originally published in *Hospital Medicine*, which cover the various aspects of publishing, writing and accessing information.

The idea for the series originated in the Publishers Association (PA) Medical Group. The series was devised by Dr Jack Tinker and the editorial team at *Hospital Medicine*, together with myself, as Managing Director of the Royal Society of Medicine Press, and a former Chair of the PA Medical Group. There are close links between the publishers in this group and medical authors and customers, and a mutuality of interest between authors and publishers in ensuring the widest possible dissemination of medical writing.

I am very grateful to the various authors for contributing their chapters and expertise to this book, and also to Binkie Mais and Tamzin Ewers of Quay Books for making it a reality.

I hope that health practitioners, especially those in training, will find that this text contains some useful pointers to help them in their careers, and I would welcome any comments or suggestions from readers.

Peter Richardson
Managing Director
Royal Society of Medicine Press
peter.richardson@rsm.ac.uk
April 2002

1

Finding health information on the Internet: health professionals

Robert Kiley

This chapter discusses some of the key problems that clinicians encounter when searching the Internet for health information. Guidance is provided on how best to search the Internet to find high-quality information and resources. The Internet is a dynamic and valuable source of information for health professionals, but information accessed through the Internet should be critically evaluated before being applied to practice.

Introduction

Information is one commodity health professionals are not short of. Official guidelines, executive letters and circulars, as well as information from professional bodies and numerous patient groups fill the clinicians' in-box with alarming regularity. In addition, there is the need to keep abreast of the research literature. In an average year around 400 000 new citations are added to the Medline database. In the words of Muir Gray (1998), 'busy clinicians are now caught in an information paradox — overwhelmed with information but unable to find the knowledge they need when they need it'.

This sense of information overload has been further exacerbated in recent years with the rise of the Internet. A survey conducted by the NEC Research Institute (2000) in January 2000 calculated that the indexable web — those pages that can be identified and indexed by search engines — consisted of approximately one billion pages, while growth was estimated to be in the order of twenty million pages a month. Precisely how many of these pages are relevant to health professionals is impossible to say, but a number of authors (Eysenbach *et al*, 1999; Kiley, 1999) have speculated that there are approximately 100 000 sites on the web that provide health information and services.

Some of the key problems clinicians face when searching the Internet for health information are discussed and guidance is offered on how best to search the Internet to find high-quality information and resources.

Key problems

A search for 'arthritis' on the popular search engine AltaVista http://www.altavista.com neatly illustrates the key problems clinicians experience when searching the Internet: too many web pages are found (this search identified over 725 000 pages), and the quality of the sites to which you are directed is highly variable. The results from the AltaVista search direct Internet users to two similar sounding sites but with vastly contrasting information.

The Cure Arthritis website http://www.curearthritis.org is the official site of the Arthritis National Research Foundation and provides information about ongoing research into the prevention and treatment of arthritis. In contrast, the Cure Arthritis — Stop Pain Now website http://www.cure-arthritis.com promotes a 'cure' for arthritis that is 'fast, easy, safe, effective, natural and permanent'. (Since this chapter was written this site is no longer accessible.)

However, numerous other sites are still selling miracle cures for arthritis such as 'The CMO solution for arthritis' at: http://www.arthritis.net/cmo.htm.)

Although identifying which is the more credible source is not particularly demanding, time and effort may nevertheless have been expended in accessing this type of website. In addition, the clinician may have to spend further time explaining to patients that the 'CMO solution' offered by the cure-arthritis.com site is nothing other than a food supplement and is unlikely to have any effect on the patient's arthritic condition.

Consequently, to minimise the time spent surfing sites such as these a different approach to searching is required. A hierarchical approach using four different levels is outlined.

Level 1: Bibliographic databases

Perhaps the best place to start any search for health information is on the traditional bibliographic databases, such as Medline, newer evidence-based sources such as the Cochrane Library, and databases that have been developed by the NHS Centre for Reviews and Dissemination.

These databases are available in formats other than the web (CD-ROM and paper, for example), but their migration to the web in recent years means that they can now be accessed through the standard web browser. Consequently, clinicians no longer have to learn how individual software applications work, or bother about installing software and regular database updates. The sources identified below are available free of charge.

Medline

❖ http://www.pubmed.gov

Developed by the US National Library of Medicine, Medline provides users with access to more than ten million citations, indexed from over 4000 biomedical journals published in more than seventy countries. The current version of PubMed contains dynamic links to related databases, such as OMIM (Online Mendelian Inheritance in Man) and protein sequences, as well as direct links to full-text articles hosted on various publisher websites. As of February 2002, 2632 full-text online journals are linked to PubMed. Help on how to search this database can be found at: http://www.rsm.ac.uk/hii/toc15.htm

Cochrane Database of Systematic Reviews

❖ http://www.update-software.com/cochrane/

The Cochrane Database of Systematic Reviews is a collection of structured and systematic reviews on the effects of health care. In the main, Cochrane reviews are based on reviews of randomised controlled trials (RCTs). Where possible, results from individual RCTs are combined statistically, with meta-analysis, to increase the power of the findings of numerous studies each too small to produce reliable results individually.

The abstracts of these reviews — which include the background to the review, search strategy, main results and conclusions — are available free of charge. If you wish to access the full-text of each review the cost for twelve months' personal access to this product is £132.00. Further details can be found at: http://www.update-software.com /cochrane/order.htm

NHS Centre for Reviews and Dissemination

❖ http://agatha.york.ac.uk/welcome.htm

The NHS Centre for Reviews and Dissemination was established to identify and review the results of good-quality health research and to disseminate actively the findings to key decision makers in the NHS. Two databases have been developed to help realise this objective: DARE (Database of Abstracts of Reviews of Effectiveness) is a database of high-quality systematic research reviews of the effectiveness of healthcare interventions; NEED (NHS Economic Evaluation Database) is a database of structured abstracts on economic evaluations of healthcare interventions.

TRIP

❖ http://www.tripdatabase.com/

TRIP (Turning Research into Practice) is an amalgamation of twenty-five databases of hyperlinks from 'evidence-based' sites around the world. At present there are over 23,000 links to evidence-based topics. Sources for this database include publications such as *Bandolier*, and *Effective Healthcare Bulletins*, as well as database services such as National Guideline Clearinghouse and POEM (Patient-Oriented Evidence that Matters).

Other databases

Other useful bibliographic databases available on the web without charge, include BioethicsLine http://www.pubmed.gov, (useful for identifying research that examines the ethical implications of biomedical research), and CancerLit http://www.cancer.gov/search/cancer_literature/ developed by the National Cancer Institute. (Note: BioethicsLine is now part of the PubMed MEDLINE database. To limit a search to articles that focus on bioethical issues, use the Limits > Subsets > Bioethics menu option.)

Level 2: Evaluated subject gateways

Research from Media Metrix (2000) shows that search engines are the most trafficked sites on the Internet. Figures for March 2000 on the top five sites — in terms of visitors — were all search sites, such as Yahoo!, Excite and Lycos. As discussed above, these tools typically identify too many sites, none of which have been assessed for quality. Sorting the wheat from the chaff is left to the individual searcher.

To mitigate this problem evaluated Internet subject gateways, rather than the generic search engines, should be used to identify high-quality health resources on the web. Only those Internet resources that meet a defined quality threshold are indexed in these gateway services. Three of the most useful health gateways, OMNI (Organising Medical Networked Information), Medical Matrix and Netting the Evidence, are discussed.

OMNI

❖ http://omni.ac.uk/

Describing itself as the UK's gateway to high-quality biomedical Internet resources, OMNI provides descriptions and links to around 5000 health websites. In contrast to the 725 000 sites identified at AltaVista, an OMNI search for arthritis points the user to just forty-one websites. All sites that are indexed by OMNI meet the quality criterion as published at: http://omni.ac.uk/agec/evalguid.html

Medical Matrix

❖ http://www.medmatrix.org/

Aimed primarily at American physicians, resources included in this database are ranked according to their utility for point-of-care clinical application. As with OMNI, there are around 5000 resources described in the Matrix, all of which are organised within a simple subject-based hierarchical structure.

Netting the Evidence

❖ http://www.nettingtheevidence.org.uk/

Compiled by Andrew Booth from the School of Health and Related Research (ScHARR), Netting the Evidence is a comprehensive, annotated guide to evidence-based healthcare resources on the Internet.

Level 3: General search tools

Because the evaluated subject gateway services are compiled manually — individuals have to visit sites, check that they meet the relevant quality criteria, and write a brief description of that service — the number of resources they point to is relatively small. Inevitably, there are times when a broader search is required. The two services described here, Google and AlltheWeb, can help the clinician conduct an effective Internet search.

Finding a website of a known organisation — Google

❖ http://www.google.com

A cursory examination of the MetaCrawler MetaSpy site http://www.metaspy.com/ (which shows in real-time what searches are currently being conducted on the MetaCrawler search site) highlights the fact that search engines are often used to identify the website of a known organisation. When faced with this problem, the Google search engine is without doubt the most effective tool currently available.

Unlike other search engines, Google returns a list of search results where the ranking is based on how other sites link to that site. And, as most hypertext links on the web point to home pages — rather than to some specific page buried deep within the site — Google searches invariably identify first the home page of any organisation. The Google developers are so confident of their search software that they invite users to select the 'I'm feeling lucky' button after a search term has been entered. On selecting this, users bypass the traditional search results page and instead are taken directly to the site that Google ranks as being the most relevant to that search.

Advanced searching — AlltheWeb

http://www.alltheweb.com/advanced

Using the 'Advanced Search' option at AlltheWeb, it is possible to conduct a highly-focused search that identifies a small number of highly-relevant sites. For example, if you were trying to find data on waiting times, a search could be constructed that only finds those sites where the word 'waiting' appears in the title of the page, and where the domain is either '.nhs.uk' or '.gov.uk'.

Level 4: Newsgroups and discussion lists

Internet discussion lists and newsgroups are another rich source of information. Although much of the debate in these forums is of an anecdotal nature, they nevertheless provide an inside into the current opinions and concerns of both health consumers and professionals.

Google groups

❖ http://groups.google.com

With the number of newsgroups now in excess of 30 000, catering for virtually every interest and hobby, identifying relevant newsgroups can be a time-consuming process. However, using the Google groups search engine, it is possible to identify quickly relevant groups. For example, a search for 'arthritis' suggests that the newsgroups alt.support.arthritis and misc.support.arthritis are the most relevant. All postings made to such newsgroups over the past twenty years (over 700 million messages) are accessible through the Google groups service.

Tile

❖ http://www.tile.net/

Similar in nature to the Interest Finder, the Tile service provides a searchable directory to over 90 000 discussion lists. A search here for discussion lists that may be of interest, for example, to an orthopaedic surgeon, identifies a number of potentially relevant forums, including one run by the Orthopaedic Trauma Association.

Evaluating what you find

Because anyone can publish anything they like on the Internet —
there is no peer-review process to thwart the hobbyist, extremist etc
— it is important that everyone evaluates the information that they
find. This topic is covered in *Chapter 2*, along with details of a
number of online tools that have been designed to develop critical
appraisal skills.

Conclusion

The Internet offers a wealth of information for all health
professionals. From databases and full-text journals to multimedia
teaching packages, telemedical applications and online
discussion forums, the Internet has the potential to meet the
information needs of all clinicians. Why this potential has not yet
been realised has, in many respects, been a result of the difficulty
in finding the truly useful, evidence-based resources that are
available on the web.

This chapter has addressed some of the most common
difficulties in finding relevant evidence-based information on the
Internet by highlighting a range of resources that can be used to
identify relevant and high-quality information.

Key points

- ✖ Information overload is a problem that all health professionals face.

- ✖ Popular search engines are not the best way to search for health information on the Internet.

- ✖ Using a mix of bibliographic databases and evaluated subject gateways is the most effective way of finding high-quality medical information.

- ✖ Discussion lists and newsgroups are a rich source of information and should not be overlooked.

- ✖ Internet information is not subject to review and therefore should be critically evaluated.

References

Eysenbach G, Sa ER, Diepgen TL (1999) Shopping around the Internet today and tomorrow: towards the millennium of cybermedicine. *Br Med J* **319**: 1294

online at: http://www.bmj.com/cgi/content/full/319/7220/1294

Kiley R (1999) Internet statistics. *Health Information on the Internet* **2**(10): 1–2

online at:http://www.rsm.ac.uk/hii/toc10.htm

Media Metrix (2000) http://www.relevantknowledge.com/Data/thetop.jsp

Muir Gray JA (1998) Where is the chief knowledge officer? *Br Med J* **317**: 832–40

online at: http://www.bmj.com/cgi/content/full/317/7162/832

NEC Research Institute http://www.neci.nj.Nec.com/neci-website/index-page.html

2

Finding health information on the Internet: health consumers

Robert Kiley

The quality of health information on the Internet is extremely variable. This chapter highlights some of the problems consumers encounter when searching for health information and suggests ways in which these can be overcome.

Introduction

A recent article in *The Independent* (Dobson, 1999) discussed a new epidemic that is terrorising today's health professional. Known as 'Internet printout syndrome' this condition usually manifests itself in the form of a 'thick wad of printouts, downloaded from the Internet' (Brown, 2000) that are presented during a consultation.

Patients and their carers are increasingly turning to the Internet for information. The reasons for this are many; to seek a second opinion, to be better informed, or to seek support from fellow patients and, as a consequence, the balance of power in the doctor–patient relationship is now changing. Information that was once the exclusive prerogative of the health professional is now available to anyone who can access the Internet.

The high level of interest in online health information can

be shown in many ways. For example, a survey undertaken by Harris and Associates (2000) estimated that in the past twelve months some sixty million American citizens went online in search of health information. In the UK, figures from the NHS Direct Online service show that in the first four weeks of operation the site attracted over seven million hits. Finally, figures from Alexa http://www.alexa.com indicate that the PubMed Medline service is one the top 400 most visited sites on the Internet.

The quality of health information on the Internet is, however, extremely variable. This chapter highlights some of the problems that consumers encounter when searching for health information, and suggests ways of overcoming them.

Health information on the Web: current problems

Within the results page of a simple search on 'cancer' one can move almost seamlessly from authoritative sites like CancerNet http://www.cancer.gov/cancer_information/ and OncoLink http://oncolink.upenn.edu/ to highly dubious sites, such as Dr Clark's 'Cancer can now be cured' site http://www.drclark.net/. Here, for example, visitors are informed that:

> *... all cancers are alike. They are all caused by a parasite... and if you kill this parasite, the cancer stops immediately.*

In the light of this statement one should not be surprised to learn that:

> *Electricity can now be used to kill bacteria, viruses and parasites in minutes, not days or weeks as antibiotics require. If you have been suffering from a chronic infection or have cancer, or AIDS, learn to build the*

> *electronic device that will stop it immediately (or buy one). It is safe and without side-effects and does not interfere with any treatment you are now on.*

Another page at this site http://www.Drclark.net/disease/zap_pix.htm provides readers with an opportunity to buy the 'electronic device' known as the 'New Super Zapper DeLuxe' for $149.99. Quite what this does is difficult to say, but what is certain is that it is not a cure for cancer.

Information bias is another problem health consumers need to be alert to. The official sounding 'National Vaccine Information Center' http://www.909shot.com/ is a national, non-profit educational organisation founded by parents whose children were injured or died following vaccine reactions. Not surprisingly, the site presents a fairly one-sided and negative view of childhood vaccinations. On the home page, for example, one can read about a thriving two-month-old baby who died after being given the diphtheria-pertussis-tetanus (DPT) vaccine, and of a thirteen-day-old baby who died following a hepatitis B injection. Although it is important that such concerns are brought to the attention of parents, equally there is a need to balance this information with the positive benefits of childhood immunisation.

Finally, most consumers have not had the benefit of many years of medical education. Consequently, even if the information retrieved is accurate and evidence-based there are still potential problems. For example, most consumers are not in a position to know whether information found on the web would be suitable for their condition — it may be contraindicated by other medication currently being prescribed — or even whether the treatment suggested is available. Viagra (sildenafil) was licensed in the USA some six months before it was available in the UK.

In the light of these problems the solution may be to try and discourage patients from using the Internet for health information. I do not believe such a strategy is either sustainable or wise. Figures from the Office of National Statistics (ONS) indicate that 38% of UK households have Internet access (ONS, 2001). Research shows that providing consumers with information about treatment choices reduces anxiety (Fallowfield *et al*, 1990), promotes a more effective relationship with health professionals (Meredith *et al*, 1995), and can lead to improved health outcomes (Brody *et al*, 1989).

Consequently, a better strategy may be to help consumers use the Internet effectively. This can be achieved by:

- directing consumers to high-quality gateway services
- alerting consumers to the need to appraise critically the information
- encouraging consumers to discuss the results of their research with health professionals.

Consumer information gateways

Over the past few years a number of consumer-focused health information gateways have been established. The purpose of these is to direct users to Internet resources that meet a defined quality criterion. Three of the most authoritative sites are discussed below.

Medlineplus

❖ http://www.nlm.nih.gov/medlineplus

Developed by the National Library of Medicine, Medlineplus directs visitors to selected online publications, web sites, and self-help groups that produce reliable information for the public. On using the A–Z health topics list someone interested in, for example, osteoporosis is directed to publications authored by bodies such as the American Academy of Orthopaedic Surgeons, the National Osteoporosis Foundation and the National Institutes of Health. Within each disease topic, resources are divided into more specific categories, thus enabling the user to focus on his/her area of interest. In the case of osteoporosis, subtopics available to the user include clinical trials, diagnosis, therapy, pictures, and statistics.

In addition, Medlineplus provides access to 'clickable' Medline searches. Thus, someone interested in finding out the latest research into the prevention of osteoporosis is presented with a single hypertext link. On hitting this, a predefined search — using all the appropriate medical subject headings (MeSH) and subheadings along with Boolean operators and limits — is executed. By accessing Medline in this way health consumers can identify current, peer-reviewed research without having to learn how to search and understand this large and complex database.

NHS Direct Online

❖ http://www.nhsdirect.nhs.uk

NHS Direct Online is the UK equivalent to Medlineplus. Although this service is not as fully developed as Medlineplus, it does provide a useful starting point for UK consumers.

The site includes an online encyclopaedia that provides diagnosis and treatment information on over 400 common conditions, and a healthy living section that gives information on reducing the risk of major diseases.

NHS Direct also provides access to the main NHS UK site http://www.nhs.uk/localnhsservices/default.asp, through which you can identify dental practices, GP surgeries, opticians and pharmacies by locality.

Patient.UK

❖ http://www.patient.co.uk

Launched in April 1998, some eighteen months before NHS Direct Online went live, this site aims to provide a comprehensive listing of UK patient-orientated web sites. Developed and run by two GPs from Newcastle, the site can be both searched and browsed. When browsing, the user can select one of twenty-eight broad subject categories — child health, diseases and illnesses — while the more focused user can use the cross-referenced alphabetical index.

Continuing with the osteoporosis example, patient.co.uk provides links to sources such as the UK National Osteoporosis Society, online fact sheets and articles published in the *British Medical Journal*.

Critical appraisal

In addition to directing users to high-quality gateway sites, health professionals should also alert consumers to the need to appraise critically the information that they find. In the main, resources found through the sites discussed above will be of high quality. However, there will be times when these services do not provide the answer to the question and a broader search, using general Internet search engines like Google and AlltheWeb, is required.

As virtually anyone can publish on the web, it is important to appraise critically the information that is found. In particular, health consumers should be suspicious of 'miracle cures' and sites which offer no independent evidence to substantiate their claims. Based on the work by Silberg *et al* (1997), any medical web page that fails to comply with the minimum standards set out below should be rejected:

Authorship

The author(s) of a web page, along with their affiliations and credentials should be clearly stated.

Attribution

If a web site is citing research as evidence then the source of this data must be stated.

Disclosure

The owner of the web site should be prominently displayed, along with any sponsorship, or advertising deals which could constitute a conflict of interest.

Currency

Web pages should state when they were created, and last updated.

A number of online tools have been created to help develop critical appraisal skills, including Discern http://www.discern.org.uk and the Information Quality (IQ) Tool http://hitiweb.mitretek.org/iq/default.asp. Both of these services provide a list of questions and discussion points that consumers need to be aware of when evaluating a site's strengths and weaknesses.

Open discussion

An article in the *Medical Journal of Australia*, on the changing role of the doctor in the Internet age, concluded that, 'it is time to embrace the concept of the informed patient and use their web-surfing skills' (Pemberton and Goldblatt, 1998). Patients and their families often have more time to search the Internet than their GPs and can limit their search to just one clinical condition, and as a consequence will come across information that the doctor is unaware of.

To help minimise the danger that scarce and expensive consultation time may be spent looking at potentially worthless information, Pemberton recommends that professionals adopt more proactive strategies. Suggestions include asking patients to send the information they have found in advance of the consultation, and advocating that health professionals set up their own web pages which direct patients to high-quality, evidence-based information.

Conclusion

The Internet offers opportunities and threats to today's information-seeking health consumer. Information on the web can be inaccurate, biased, and even harmful. On the other hand, used judiciously and with active support from professionals, this new medium presents everyone with the opportunity to become active and informed partners in the healthcare process.

Key points

⌘ The quality of health information on the Internet is extremely variable.

⌘ Patients are increasingly turning to the Internet to find health information.

⌘ The doctor–patient relationship is changing as patients become better informed about health care.

⌘ Health professionals need to develop strategies to help consumers use the Internet effectively.

⌘ Evaluated gateway services are a recommended starting point for information-seeking consumers.

⌘ Patients need to develop critical appraisal skills.

References

Brody DS, Miller SM, Lerman CE, Smith DG, Caputo GC (1989) Patient perception of involvement in medical care: relationships to illness, attitudes and outcomes. *J Gen Int Med* **4**: 506–11

Brown H (2000) Internet printout syndrome. *Heath Information on the Internet* **13**: 3

Dobson R (1999) Doctors plagued by patients getting second opinion from the internet. A new epidemic is terrorising our GPs: internet printout syndrome.
The Independent 6 December: 3

Fallowfield LJ, Hall A, Macguire GP, Baum M (1990) Psychological outcomes of different treatment policies in women with early breast cancer outside a clinical trial. *Br Med J* **301**: 575–80

Harris L *et al* (2000) Sixty million seek health info online in the US. online: http://www.nua.ie/surveys/index. cgi?f=VS&art_id=905354697&rel=true

Meredith P, Emberton M, Wood C (1995) New directions in information for patients. *Br Med J* **311**: 4–5

Office of National Statistics (2001) Internet access: 2nd quarter 2001 online: http://www.statistics.gov.uk/pdfdir/int0901.pdf

Pemberton PJ, Goldblatt J (1998) The Internet and the changing roles of doctors, patients and families. *Med J Aust* **169**: 594–5 online: http://www.mja.com.au/public/issues/xmas98/pemberton/pemberton.html

Silberg WM, Lundberg GD, Musacchio RA (1997) Assessing, controlling and assuring the quality of medical information on the Internet: caveant lector et viewor. Let the reader and viewer beware. *JAMA* **227**: 1244–5

3

Writing a case report: an editor's eye view

Robin Fox

'That was a nice presentation. Why not write it up for a journal?' With such words a thousand case reports are born. But they are like birds tossed over a stormy ocean: only a few gain a foothold in the rigging of passing ships — for the rest, oblivion. So, how do you persuade an editor to accept your wonderful case report? Here are some reflections from the editor's standpoint.

What are you trying to achieve?

First, and most important, understand that most journals do not exist primarily to serve authors. Their mission is to stimulate and educate and entertain their readers. Clever editors and authors arrange for these interests to coincide.

For the best chance of success, you must begin by thinking strategically — about the purpose of your report, who could benefit from reading it, and how to make it stand out from the competition. In the hierarchy of evidence-based medicine, randomised controlled trials come top and case reports near the bottom, so you might think that a case report deserves only a modest investment of time and energy. If you have any such notion (or even if you do not), you are advised to read a subtle critique by the epidemiologist JP Vandenbroucke (1999) who argues that: 'For true intellectual advancement, ie. in proposing new problems, new solutions, or new ideas, the hierarchy is... reversed.'

In the age of evidence-based medicine, Vandenbroucke declares, case reports remain as necessary as ever — but he also remarks that, 'the days of droning out one case after another, as an excuse for a haphazard literature review, are over.'

So, what are you hoping to achieve by getting your case report into print? Publication may be good for your career prospects and can also be a stimulating experience, but let us set aside these personal aspects. What are you seeking to do for the readers? In his taxonomy of case reports, Vandenbroucke offers the following headings:

- descriptions of new diseases
- aetiology and recognition of side-effects
- study of mechanisms
- therapy and prognosis
- education
- quality assurance.

Most editors will prefer the first three, but what they receive is mainly the last two. An 'educational' report might serve to remind readers of some neglected complex of symptoms or signs, and the 'quality assurance' category might be an instructive tale of accident or error. The real challenge is to avoid 'droning out one case after another'. Whatever the category, the key element of a good case report, according to Vandenbroucke, is surprise — the 'discovery' aspect, both scientific and educational, that 'makes them such great fun to read, to discuss and to present.' For the full argument read the original, but let me offer one further quotation:

> *Besides clearly formulating the point you want to make, you should preferably also specify the strong prior expectation that forms the basis of your report. That will make it obvious to the readers why they should be*

> *surprised. The expectation can be a 'mental control group',*
> *based on theory or on the shared experience of physicians,*
> *or it can be derived from the published work...*

Allied to the purpose of your report is the intended audience. The style and language will depend greatly on whether you are addressing fellow specialists or the multidisciplinary readership of the *British Medical Journal* or *Hospital Medicine*.

Writing it

Four decades ago, Richard Asher (1958) asked: 'Why are medical journals so dull?' One of his complaints was that published reports followed a ritual far removed from the excitement of the clinical pursuit. His words still strike a chord. Good style is partly a matter of structure. Must you give the game away right at the start, in the title or the introduction, or might the case be presented more as it evolved, with clues to the diagnosis accumulating as the story goes on?

Asher refers to a case report which began with his reading an editorial (recent past), then remembering a patient (from ten years ago), tracing her, and describing her behaviour when she attended a clinical meeting (today). *The Lancet*, for its case reports, favours the 'puzzle' approach, and uses titles such as 'An Asian man with enlarged glands', or 'A boy with chickenpox whose fingers peeled'. Admittedly, this is not ideal for presentation of original findings — especially if the journal does not publish abstracts or keywords for case reports.

If you wish the report to be cited in future publications you will doubtless opt for an explanatory title. But one reason for the dullness of medical journals is that authors cater for tomorrow's researchers at the expense of today's readers.

You have done all the background reading and decided what and who your report is for. Now you can start work on the central part, the case history. You sit at the keyboard and, if you are at all typical, rattle out something like, 'A fifty-five-year old man presented with...' (Nine out of ten case reports sent to the *Journal of the Royal Society of Medicine* begin in this way — and I sometimes wonder who started the rot.) Apart from the lack of originality, isn't 'presented' an odd word to use these days for a person seeking medical help? And must every person be immediately defined by age? Perhaps because of their origin in medical meetings, where jargon is permissible, case reports are peculiarly subject to hackneyed phraseology and cliché, of which my least favourite at present is, 'demonstrates the need for a high index of suspicion' (usual translation — 'how astute we were').

But all this, you may say, is mere nit-picking, nothing to do with the quality of the report which went down so well at the clinical meeting. True, but for a journal that aims to serve readers, style does matter. Real scientific excellence will usually win through, but if the editor has to choose between two items of equal and modest scientific merit, an imaginative presentation can make the difference between success and failure.

Sending it in

You have now added an introduction and a discussion, shown the final text to your co-authors and obtained their signed agreement, and checked the text one last time for typing errors (carelessness is deeply unpopular with editors and reviewers). You have also looked at the journal, to see how it prints articles of this sort, and followed all the instructions to the authors.

Now for the covering letter: 'Dear Sir/Madam, I enclose a case report and look forward to hearing from you...' No! You may feel that a bland letter of this kind is the correct form, since the editorial evaluation will be objective and the merit of your article will speak for itself. This is a delusion. You are not dealing with a sorting office or a quality control system but with a dynamic process in which the editor's priorities will change from day-to-day according to what papers are in hand, popular topics of the day and perhaps even the state of his or her digestion.

Sifting through the week's pile of submissions, the editor will conduct a sort of triage in which your paper may become an immediate victim. One editorial question may be, 'why this journal?'; another, 'what have we done on this subject recently?' The editorial catch-22 is: 'If the condition is rare, one more case will be of scant general interest; if it is common, what can one more case contribute?'

In your covering letter, you have an opportunity to explain, and thus improve your chances. Say just how well your observations fit in with what the journal has published over the past year or so, and why they will interest the readers. Editors are proud of their journals and are human: if you fail to spot that the subject has been covered in a recent issue, you may damage your chances of success.

Reactions from reviewers

If your paper survives this editorial assessment, the next hurdle is peer review; and, here again, do not expect complete objectivity. The report often comes down to 'I enjoyed it'. Many clinician-scientists will scorn a case report that does not offer some original observation, so a kindly editor has to choose the reviewers accordingly. The reports that fare best in peer review, I find, are those in Vandenbroucke's last category — stories of accident and error. They arouse sympathy — in contrast to those designed to illustrate exemplary management, which invite criticism.

A common non-scientific complaint from reviewers is that, although 'authorship' includes every clinician who laid hands on the patient, there is no mention whatever of the radiologist or histopathologist or microbiologist who provided crucial information (a particularly common objection from reviewers who are radiologists, histopathologists or microbiologists). Authorship is handled too casually, I find.

Ask not...

Many of the case reports that are offered to the *Journal of the Royal Society of Medicine* might be described as pedestrian, but a well-done report gives me satisfaction as an editor; and some of my readers seem happier reading about a single patient than the report of a randomised trial in 200. Nevertheless, many journals now declare the case report unwelcome, and competition for the remaining slots is such that special efforts are required to gain a place. Follow my advice and you will certainly improve your chances with the *Journal of the Royal Society of Medicine*; for other journals I can promise nothing.

My parting message is, do not cast your paper haphazardly into the stormy air. Aim it carefully at the editor you most favour. And ask not what the journal can do for you, but what you can do for the journal.

Key points

- ⌘ The vital element in a good case report is surprise — an observed event compared with expectations.
- ⌘ The author should have a clear idea of the purpose of the report, scientific or educational.
- ⌘ There is no standard format: if dullness is to be avoided, the structure and phrasing of a case report demand creative thought.
- ⌘ The report should be written with a particular journal and readership in mind.

References

Asher R (1958) Why are medical journals so dull? *Br Med J* **ii**: 502–3

Vandenbroucke JP (1999) Case reports in an evidence-based world. *J R Soc Med* **92**: 159–63

4

How to write a book

Roger S Kirby

> *Doctors write books primarily to gain recognition from their peers and credibility with their patients. The key steps involve careful planning of the project, finding the right publisher, ensuring the text is completed on time, and scrupulous checking of the proofs. The end product should be something of which the author is justifiably proud.*

As a busy doctor, what on earth would compel you to write a book? There are all sorts of motives, but most do it for recognition by their patients and peers. It is also very fulfilling to see your own thoughts and views on display in printed form. Although less academically prestigious than peer-reviewed papers, books usually appeal to a wider audience and bestow their own particular credibility on the author. The potential for royalties should also not be discounted.

Getting started

So how to set about the task? First decide upon your subject. What is the competition in terms of other books in the area? A literature search is essential and it is worth asking around if there are already other titles in the pipeline. Do not be too put off by similar competitor titles, however; there are very few areas of medicine that are covered by a single book on the subject.

Second, decide upon your audience. Are you writing for specialists in the area, GPs, patients or the general public? Clearly the style and content will need to be targeted accordingly.

Finally, you need to find a publisher. A recurring complaint from my colleagues who have written books is that they feel their publishers have not marketed their volumes properly. This certainly is an important consideration; in general, smaller publishers have fewer resources to undertake mail shots and to make sure that the book is displayed on the bookstands at appropriate meetings of specialist societies. Ask around and find a publisher with a good track record. Try and speak to some of the authors who have worked with them. What were their experiences? Did they get the support that they needed? Did they receive their royalties promptly and in full?

Once you have decided on your subject and you have a publisher interested, he or she will require an outline of proposed chapters, their contents and a list of potential authors. At this stage you need to decide whether to:

1. Write a monograph yourself.
2. Work with two or three colleagues, dividing the subject up according to their interests and expertise.
3. Edit, or co-edit, a full-blown multi-author textbook.

Personally, I prefer the first or second options, because the third involves the rather tiresome task of chasing those contributors whose chapters are always 'in the pipeline' and never on your desk. Moreover, in the new word of e-publishing and web sites, the importance of the 'standard text' seems likely to decline. If you choose to work with colleagues and friends, make sure that they share your commitment to the task and preferably have some previous writing experience. There is nothing more dispiriting than having to rewrite other authors' sections because they are not up to scratch.

At this stage, you and your co-authors will each be sent a

contract from the publisher. You should read this carefully because it is a legal document. At this point, you may need some negotiating skills because this is the time to make sure that you are happy with your royalty (Fisher *et al*, 1981). Do not be surprised if the percentage is small; most doctors publish for prestige rather than money. If you have a track record in publishing, however, you may be able to negotiate an increase in the royalty before you sign the contract. If the book is purchased and distributed by a pharmaceutical company, the royalty payment will obviously reflect the overall volume of sales.

Start writing

The next step is to get started on the writing (Kirby, 2000). Time management is critical. First make a detailed plan. I usually 'free write' my ideas, then organise them and reorganise again so that I am sure where I am going. Then set a time frame including a start date, a completion date and progress monitoring stages. Be realistic, and add 20% extra as contingency time. It has been discovered that most of us do 80% of our productive work in 20% of our time; this is especially true of writing, which does require a great deal of focused effort. Work out when your most creative and productive period is (for most of us it is first thing in the morning) and plan out some dedicated writing time, ideally in two-hour portions, in a place where you cannot be disturbed.

Once you start, the project takes on a life of its own and the going usually gets progressively easier. Try to write directly onto a PC or laptop because this is more time efficient and often enhances writing style and composition. Do not forget to back up your files.

Write clearly and in plain English. Be simple but not simplistic. The rules of effective writing are set out in *Table 3.1*.

After you have written a section, check it carefully and if possible ask someone else, a friend, colleague or spouse, to read it and make comments. Use software such as Reference Manager™ (ISI Researchsoft, Thomson Scientific, Berkeley, California) to facilitate the referencing of the text. Do not quote every paper written on the subject, only those germane to your central argument. In general, medical writers are too sparing with illustrations because they tend to think in terms of words rather than images. In fact, a good illustration can convey a great deal of information, and save a good deal of explanatory text. In addition, illustrations help to break up blocks of text and make it more user-friendly for the reader.

Table 4.1: Rules of effective writing

Avoid trying to impress your reader with your extensive vocabulary

Try to use as few words as possible

Use short rather than long words

Use synonyms only when writing for specialists

Restrict sentences to fifteen to twenty words

Use bullet points and illustrations to break up blocks of text

Avoid clichés (like the plague!)

Use different levels of headings

Make sure arithmetic is correct and statistics accurate

Always keep your reader and your message in mind

From Kirby, 2000

Submitting the manuscript

When you are happy with your contribution, send it off in duplicate and in electronic format to your publisher with a covering letter. Then wait! After what seems an age you will receive your manuscript back with sub-editor's queries marked. Go through the text again, carefully answering the queries.

Because of the time lapse the material that you wrote will often seem quite strange. A few up-to-date references can be added but resist fiddling too much with the manuscript, just get it back to the publisher. The next stage is usually the colour proofs which are always exciting but need checking scrupulously for errors. Again, resist the temptation to change things unnecessarily, do the necessary and get them back to the publisher.

If you are working on a multi-author book then, as editor, you will also have to check the manuscripts of other contributors. This is often quite hard work, but does need to be done thoroughly. Do not worry too much about minor grammatical errors or syntax: these will be dealt with by the professional sub-editor. Your job is to look at the bigger picture. Is the message clear, is there overlap with other chapters, what is the reviewer in the *New England Journal of Medicine* going to say about this in relation to the rest of the book? You as editor have to maintain quality control. And what do you do about the recalcitrant authors who still fail to send in their manuscripts? Call them, e-mail them, write to them. Keep the pressure on. If the piece of work is still not forthcoming then you have a number of choices:

1. Drop the chapter — is it essential to the book?
2. Write it yourself or find someone else to write it in a short time frame.
3. As a last resort you could commission professional medical writers to write chapters for authors based on their published work. This is an expedient but expensive remedy.

Most books need a foreword and a preface. The foreword is an opportunity to ask an eminent colleague to endorse the book and hopefully say some flattering things about the content. The preface is contributed by the author(s) and should explain why the book was written, its basic message and for whom it is written.

Some publishers also ask you to supply the 'blurb' describing the contents for the back cover. This should not be undertaken lightly since many sales are made on the basis of potential purchasers browsing through the back cover notes. The final task is to check carefully that the author details and chapter list are correct. Reviewers love to nitpick and contributors hate to have their name spelt incorrectly.

Finally, wait until the book appears and try to persuade the publishers to fund a champagne party to celebrate the launch. Come on you budding authors, boot up your laptops and you're off.

Key points

⌘ Plan your book carefully.

⌘ Always keep your audience in mind.

⌘ Negotiate your royalties with your publisher.

⌘ Ensure you complete the project on time.

⌘ Check proofs scrupulously for errors.

References

Fisher R, Ury W, Patton B (1981) *Getting to Yes: Negotiating Agreement Without Giving In*. Penguin, London

Kirby R (2000) Effective communication. In: Kirby R, Mundy A, eds. *How to Succeed as A Hospital Doctor*. Health Press, Oxford: 55–78

5

How to get your medical book published

Peter Richardson

What do medical publishers want? What types of book sell well? How should you approach a publisher with an idea for a book? This chapter provides answers to these and other questions. Doctors with good ideas for books are in demand. But beware, success also carries penalties!

What do publishers (and authors) want?

The answer is books that sell and... well, books that sell! Certainly there may be some academic kudos and maybe even career benefit from writing a book, but most authors want lots of people to buy and read their books. While the sales of medical titles won't come close to JK Rowling and Harry Potter, sales like that should be your aspiration.

So you want to write a medical book

The first question to think about is: who is it for? Is there a clear audience? And if there is, why will people buy it? What is the particular benefit of that book to the reader? If you think about books that you buy, there will generally be a clear benefit, some definite 'added value' that you would not have had without that book. If it's a textbook, you'll get through an exam. If it's a travel guide, you won't get lost in Beijing. And so on.

The next question is: what's the competition? Why will your book be better? For just about any new book there will be existing competition. In fact, from the publisher's point of view, lack of competition could be more worrying. Lack of competition may indicate that there's no market for your book, unless, as occasionally happens, it's a genuine first and defines the field. Sackett *et al*'s *Evidence-Based Medicine: How to Practice and Teach EBM* was one such book, but they are rare.

And, finally, you need to think whether you are going to write the book yourself, or with a colleague, or maybe edit a book written by a group of contributors. The answer will depend on the type of book you're writing, and on your own temperament. It's just not possible for one or two authors these days to write a comprehensive reference book on, say, cardiology; whereas, at the other end of the scale, a short MCQ book for the MRCP would be well within a single author's grasp.

What types of book sell well?

While it's dangerous to generalise, and there are successful books outside these categories, the following come to mind:

* Student and postgraduate textbooks, exam-practice and revision books. Everyone needs to pass exams, and even with the greater emphasis on problem-based learning, learning to learn and less fact-loaded curricula, students still love books that present a subject clearly and concisely.
* Definitive tomes covering a whole specialty. By these I mean books like Braunwald's *Heart Disease*, Mandell's *Principles and Practice of Infectious Diseases*, or Wall and Melzack's

Textbook of Pain. These will invariably be multi-author and will sell internationally. One problem is that they may be out-of-date by the time they're published. Nevertheless, many are now including related websites to keep purchasers up-to-date between editions. Possibly an endangered species, but a number still make a lot of money for their publishers and editors.

❖ Books on hot topics. These can do well if published at the right time when people really need to know about a new subject. Governments in the UK and elsewhere are always obliging publishers and authors by bringing out new healthcare initiatives and buzz words, and some of these can lead to successful books. The Royal Society of Medicine's *Clinical Governance: Making It Happen* is a good example.

❖ Books on newly emerging subjects. These are hot topics that may become more permanent features on the scene. Recently, good examples have been evidence-based medicine, and health information on the Internet.

And what types of book sell badly?

❖ Radiology for Surgeons. These types of book are well-meaning and usually written by people in one specialty who think that another should know more about their subject. Maybe they should, but the question is: do they need or want to? Now that's not to say that books on team approaches and shared care cannot be popular, just that one specialist writing for another (who has no need to know) will generally not succeed.

❖ Too specialised. Gone are the days of the specialised monograph (remember when libraries bought books?) whose epitome could well have been *The Sinus Node in Pediatrics*, published in the 1970s. Books that simply have too narrow an interest will not sell.

❖ 'Me too' professional and reference books. These are the definitive tomes that don't quite make it. Maybe the size is wrong, or the contributors are not right.

❖ Historical books. Generally these can be hard to sell, but they do have a loyal following. Quite a few doctors are interested in the history of their subject, but sales of such books will never be huge.

❖ Conference proceedings. There are many excellent things about conferences, but books based on them tend not to sell well, perhaps because the papers presented at meetings are often based on data that the speaker has already published elsewhere. Having said that, doctors are generally glad to receive a book of conference proceedings free of charge, so the best route to publication for such books is often via some form of sponsorship. Occasionally, a book based on a conference presenting new information for the first time can do well.

There are other ways of making a book pay and have a wider readership than would be the case if left to normal market forces. Pharmaceutical sponsorship has been mentioned above. In addition, various bodies have grants or funds that may be used to support scholarly works, or a particular society may be prepared to purchase a bulk quantity of the book.

How to choose a publisher

Should you publish with a large corporation or a smaller company? The answer may depend on the type of book you want to write, and on how important a personal relationship is with your editor. The medical publishing corporations are notorious for changing and reorganising (rather like the NHS), which is destabilising for those working in them and for their authors.

Smaller companies may be able to give more personal attention, but may have a less impressive list of overseas offices. However, don't automatically assume that a large company is necessarily going to sell more of your book than a smaller one. Some questions to consider when deciding on a publisher are:

- do they publish the sort of book I'm interested in writing?
- how will my book fit into their list?
- are they responsive?
- can I speak to someone and get a sensible reply?
- do they answer my e-mails?
- how will they market my book?
- do I know any other authors on their list and, if so, what do they think of the publisher?
- finally, there's no substitute for meeting people from the publisher and forming your own opinion.

How to approach a publisher

Use the phone or visit the publisher's web site to find out the name of the commissioning editor for your subject (in a smaller publisher, it may be the publishing director or managing director). Telephone or e-mail them to discuss your project. Expect a prompt and informed response. Remember, it's a seller's market for good ideas.

If possible, have an outline and perhaps some sample material available to follow up any interest from the publisher. Be prepared to take on board suggestions, or even criticism — occasionally publishers themselves can come up with good ideas!

Persist if rejected. *Longitude* and *The Kon-Tiki Expedition* are both highly successful books that were rejected by over ten publishers before enriching those that finally published them. Even JK Rowling had to shop around for a publisher.

The treadmill

The penalty for success is being asked endlessly to produce new editions, but the satisfaction of having written a book that has sold and been found useful should compensate for this.

You may find yourself being asked to write other books for the same publisher, and may be approached by other publishers (some of whom will wish they'd snapped you up when you talked to them originally).

Publishers will want you to edit journals, write CD-ROMs, help them develop web sites, and so on. Forget about your family and your hobbies for the foreseeable future.

Finally

If, despite your best efforts, your book is rejected by one editor after another, just remember what Adlai Stevenson said:

> *An editor is someone who separates the wheat from the chaff — and then prints the chaff.*

Key points

- ⌘ Be clear about your intended audience.
- ⌘ Consider what benefits your book will offer them.
- ⌘ Choose your publisher carefully, and don't assume that large publishers automatically mean large sales.
- ⌘ Be prepared to cancel your spare time activities if you do write a best-seller.

6

How to write a peer review

Elisabeth Paice

The peer review process is a quality control for scientific publications. Well done, it helps editors to improve their journals and protects readers from wasting time on ill-conceived, redundant, irrelevant or erroneous literature. Badly done, it can act as an obstacle to innovation. This chapter tells you how to be a first rate peer reviewer.

What is peer review?

Most scientific journals submit papers that they are considering for publication to the process of peer review. In practice, this means identifying one or two other workers in the same field and asking their opinion about the quality of the paper concerned. Ideally, this process will provide the editor with impartial but informed advice as to whether the paper is worth publishing as it stands, and if not, how the authors might improve it.

Provided the reviewer is familiar with the subject matter, prepared to spend time on the job and sufficiently open-minded to respond to new ideas, his or her report can provide a quality check that works to the advantage of editors, authors and readers alike. Peer review is something that experts in all fields, not just medicine, seem to accept they should do, usually in their own time and for no remuneration (Huston, 1994).

Why me?

The first time you are asked to do a peer review, you are likely to ask yourself, 'Why me?' You may have been chosen because you have recently published research on a related topic yourself, and are now perceived as an expert in the field. Alternatively, you may have been selected as representative of the clinicians whose practice might be influenced by the research. Your name may have been suggested to the editor as a potential addition to the journal's list of regular peer reviewers and this simply seemed an opportunity to try you out. Research into peer reviewing has shown that the people who write the best peer reviews are from a top academic institution, aged under forty years and known to the editor (Evans *et al*, 1993). Training in epidemiology or statistics also helps. If you do not have all, or indeed any, of these characteristics, it is worth considering why they might be important and what special qualities you could offer in their place.

What the editor wants

The editor is likely to be looking for a peer reviewer who has an inside knowledge of the field and can comment on:

- whether the work adds anything new to the existing body of knowledge
- whether the methods used were appropriate and properly explained
- whether the results were of interest
- whether the discussion dealt with the weaknesses and limitations of the study
- whether the conclusions were justified by the findings.

They are not simply looking for advice as to whether to publish the paper, although they will value an opinion (Goldbeck-Wood, 1998).

Although errors or ambiguities should be pointed out, they do not want you to rewrite or copy-edit the text. They appreciate constructive criticism that can be passed to the author, even if they decide not to publish. And, of course, they want you to provide the report within a stated time or say promptly if you cannot take it on.

What the author wants

The author has a right to expect an informed, fair and confidential assessment of the submitted paper. An informed reviewer is not just an expert but one who has taken the trouble to read the paper thoroughly. It is infuriating, for example, to be criticised for 'omissions' which are actually there in the text or tables.

A fair reviewer will not make judgements based on the credentials of the 'stable' from which the research emanates, or the gender, age or ethnic origin of the researcher, but will judge the paper on its merits. A fair reviewer will also keep an open mind even when the approach or findings are contrary to their own views.

Confidentiality is a very real worry for the author, who is well aware that the peer reviewer may be a competitor in the same field. This is especially concerning when the paper is rejected, sent back for extensive revision or where the wait before publication is long. Most authors recognise that peer review has the potential to improve the quality of the paper (Sweitzer and Cullen, 1994), but constructive criticism in the context of conditional acceptance is welcome even if it means significant delay to publication.

What the reader wants

Readers like research articles to be reliable, readable and relevant to their practice (Justice *et al*, 1994). They need to be helped to see the article in the field, to appreciate the limitations and weaknesses of the approach, and to understand how the conclusions should affect their clinical practice or their own research. A good peer review will ensure that these points are addressed in the published paper. The reader would also like to be protected from ill-conceived, irrelevant, redundant or frankly erroneous papers. A study of readers of one medical journal indicated significantly increased satisfaction with articles after both peer review and editing (Jean-Pierre *et al*, 1996).

Should I do it?

Most journals will give you a deadline of two to six weeks for your report, and will ask you to return the manuscript immediately if you do not think you will be able to do it in this time. Before deciding to accept the task, you should carefully consider whether you will have the time — about three hours is usual, although it varies with the length and complexity of the paper.

Next you need to consider whether the article is appropriate for you to review. It may be too far outside your area of expertise, or it may be too close to work you are currently engaged on, presenting you with a potential conflict of interest. It may have been written by a personal friend or enemy, either of which may make it difficult to offer an unbiased opinion. It may deal with an issue about which you feel so strongly that you would not be open-minded about any contrary point of view. A quick read through the article will alert you to likely problems along these lines and allow you to withdraw.

Any reasonable editor will respect you for this response, provided it is promptly done. Whether you accept or refuse, ethically you must be bound by the confidentiality of the peer review process. This means not discussing the paper even with your own team, not referring to the work even obliquely, and trying your best to wipe your mind clear of the work until or unless it is published.

Critical appraisal

You have read the article through quickly and decided that it would be appropriate to accept the challenge. The next step is to read it through again slowly, this time mentally asking yourself questions as you go through each section (*Table 6.1*).

What was the research intended to elucidate? Why did they choose this method? When did the study take place? Where was it done? Was the method chosen appropriate? Was that sample size large enough? Was the response rate high enough? Why might non-responders have differed? What were the outcome measures? Have the authors discussed the weaknesses and limitations? Note any points at which answers to these questions are not forthcoming from the text. Do the omissions matter to the reader's understanding of the research? Where a questionnaire has been used in the research, ask the editor for a copy before embarking on the peer review. Reading the actual wording of each question may reveal unintended ambiguities that explain otherwise surprising results.

Finally ask yourself, 'So what?'. While this may seem a negative question, your attempt to answer it will help you to identify what is new or different or clinically relevant about the work. Sometimes the authors have become so immersed in presenting a mass of data that they themselves lose sight of its relevance. Judicious restructuring or clearing away irrelevant data may make the whole thing come alive and reveal the story a good paper should tell. Stop there and put the paper away until another day. Your mind will continue to work on it and when you return for the final reading before writing your report, you will be surprised at how much better you understand what the authors have done and are trying to say.

Table 6.1: Peer review checklist

Title	Does this reflect the contents?
Abstract	Is this a fair summary, properly structured?
Introduction	Does this set the work in context?
Methodology	Is it appropriate? Is it adequately described?
Subjects and setting	Is there in-built bias? Is the sample large enough?
Statistical methodology	Is this adequately described, appropriate?
Results	Are they credible? Is the response rate adequate?
Tables and figures	Are they helpful, accurate, clear, properly labelled?
Discussion	Are weaknesses and limitations explored?
Conclusions	Are they justified?
References	Are they accurate? Are important references missing?
Originality	Does this paper add anything new? Am I being open to a new idea?
Relevance	Is it of interest to the journal's readership?

Check the facts

Go through the paper again, making a note of any missing information or ambiguities you still find. Look for errors in tables, figures or references. It is common to find columns that don't add up, or that there are discrepancies between text and tables. Look up a sample of the references quoted. This may seem excessively time-consuming, but with Medline or the like it is not difficult to do. Careless errors or frank misrepresentation of citations should alert you to question the scientific data presented. At the same time, use key words to search for other papers on the subject. Peer review should help to expose errors, plagiarism or dual publication.

Preparing the report

Many editors will tell you the structure they would like your report to follow. They may ask for comments on each element of the paper, such as abstract, introduction, method, results, analysis, discussion, conclusion or references. They may include a rating scale for criteria such as originality, scientific validity or relevance to their readership.

Some will ask for an opinion on whether the paper should be published, and if so, with what priority. You may be told what aspects of the paper they wish you to comment on, for example, they may say that they have already sent the paper to their statistics expert, and it is the clinical relevance of the findings they would like your opinion about. Different kinds of papers need different approaches. A useful series of articles in the *Canadian Medical Association Journal* offers advice to both authors and peer reviewers about what makes a good case report

(Huston, 1996a), survey (Huston, 1996b), or qualitative report (Rowan, 1997). See also *Chapter 3* for advice on writing a case report.

Advice to the author

Most journals will ask for comments for the author on a separate sheet, often specifying that these should not include any comment about whether the paper should be published. These comments are often the most time-consuming part of the exercise. They should be constructive, courteous and realistic. Resist the temptation to direct the authors to your own seminal work on the subject, unaccountably missing from the references.

Judge the research for what it is, not what it might have been. Suggesting, for example, that a qualitative focus group study would have been better done as a large scale randomised controlled trial is unhelpful. The best peer review comments to authors point out ways in which the work already done could be presented more clearly, lead to more robust conclusions, or have more relevance to the reader.

Masking and blinding

Traditionally the peer reviewer has had the advantage of knowing the authors of the paper, while the authors have not known the identity of their peer reviewer. These traditions have recently become the subject of research and debate. Does keeping the identity of the peer reviewer secret from the author (masking) lead to better of worse outcomes than open reviewing? Would the reviewer feel motivated to be more thorough, or reluctant to be frank? The *British Medical Journal* carried out a randomised controlled trial of open peer review and concluded that it did not lead to higher quality opinions, but nor did it lead to poorer quality ones (van Rooyen *et al*, 1999).

Is peer review a worthwhile exercise?

The hallowed status of editorial peer review as the means of quality control in published papers has been vigorously questioned in the last few years (Bailar and Patterson, 1985; Horrobin, 1990; Rennie, 1998; Albert, 1999). Peer review has been criticised as slow, expensive, profligate of academic time, highly subjective, prone to bias, easily abused, poor at detecting gross defects and almost useless for detecting fraud.

In a study researchers took a paper about to be published in the *British Medical Journal*, inserted eight deliberate errors, and sent them to 420 potential reviewers: 221 responded. The median number of errors spotted was two, nobody spotted more than five, and 16% didn't spot any (Smith, 1997). At the same time, peer reviewers have themselves been known to behave unethically. Reviewer misconduct has included bias, plagiarism, conflict of interest and breach of confidentiality (Huston, 1994). Finally, peer reviewers with fixed ideas may block publication of papers that take a different approach or come up with contrary findings to their own.

All peer review can reasonably do is detect major defects of originality and scientific credibility, together with commenting on important omissions, the rigour of the arguments and defects in the writing style. Peer review does not and cannot ensure perfection; the final judge for the quality of any reported work must remain the test of time (Lock, 1994).

The future of peer review

With the advent of the Internet the possibilities have opened up for scientists and clinicians to 'publish' their findings, without having to convince gatekeepers on the way (Albert, 1997). This prospect may excite frustrated authors, but strikes dread into the hearts of clinicians already struggling to keep abreast of the explosion in medical knowledge. A system in which impartial experts prevent pointless, repetitive, or frankly incorrect research results from adding to the global information glut is clearly desirable.

One major problem with peer review appears to be lack of critical assessment skills. A formal curriculum in the fundamentals of peer reviewing, a credentialling process for peer reviewers, a set of broadly agreed criteria for peer review quality, tracking of performance to detect 'doves' and 'hawks' and the development of more effective mechanisms for applying those criteria all seem to be worth serious consideration (Davidoff, 1996).

The second problem appears to be lack of remunerated time for the peer reviewer to do the job properly. Journals pay their peer reviewers little or nothing for the job, relying on the good nature, interest, desire for influence, or 'noblesse oblige' in the academic world (Huston, 1994). Perhaps it would be an advantage for a journal to train and pay for a small team of experienced professionals. On the other hand, the likely gain in rigour of such an approach might be counterbalanced by the loss of the interest and empathy the best peer reviewers bring to the task of evaluating each other's results. For the moment the job is still there to be done, and the rewards are in the opportunity you will have to exercise your critical appraisal skills, in the insights you will gain about what makes a paper publishable, and in your consciousness of being useful to the scientific community of which you are a part.

Key points

⌘ Respect the needs of editor, author and reader.

⌘ Use a checklist to ensure that you cover all aspects of the task.

⌘ Help the author to make the most of what has been done.

⌘ Don't break confidentiality.

⌘ Say you will do it only if you can offer expertise, effort and impartiality.

References

Albert T (1997) Why bother with peer review? *Lancet* **350**: 822

Albert T (1999) Thinking the unthinkable. *Br Med J* **319**: 861

Bailar JC, Patterson K (1985) Journal peer review: the need for a research agenda. *N Engl J Med* **312**: 645–57

Davidoff F (1996) Masking, blinding, and peer review: the blind leading the blinded. *Ann Intern Med* **128**: 66–8

Evans AT, McNutt RA, Fletcher SW, Fletcher RH (1993) Characteristics of peer reviewers who produce good reviews. Second International Congress on Peer Review in Biomedical Publication. American Medical Association, Chicago: 11

Goldbeck-Wood S (1998) What makes a good reviewer of manuscripts? The BMJ invites you to join its peer review process. *Br Med J* **316**: 86

Horrobin DF (1990) The philosophical basis of peer review and the suppression of innovation. *JAMA* **263**: 1438–41

Huston P (1994) Information for peer reviewers. *Can Med Assoc J* **150**: 1211–16

Huston P (1996a) Case reports: information for authors and peer reviewers. *Can Med Assoc J* **154**: 43–4

Huston P (1996b) Reporting on surveys: information for authors and peer reviewers. *Can Med Assoc J* **154**: 1695–8

Jean-Pierre ENP, Walvoort HC, Overbeke A, John PM (1996) Readers' evaluation of effect of peer review and editing on quality of articles in the Nederlands Tijdschrift voor Geneeskunde. *Lancet* **348**: 1480–3

Justice AC, Berlin JA, Fletcher SW, Fletcher RH, Goodman SN (1994) Do readers and peer reviewers agree on manuscript quality? *JAMA* **272**: 117–19

Justice AC, Cho MK, Winker MA, Berlin JA, Rennie D (1998) Does masking author identity improve peer review quality?: A randomized controlled trial. *JAMA* **280**: 240–2

Laband D (1994) A citation analysis of the impact of blinded peer review. *JAMA* **272**: 147–9

Lock S (1994) Does editorial peer review work? *Ann Intern Med* **121**: 60–1

Rennie D (1998) Peer review in Prague. *JAMA* **280**: 214–5

Rowan M (1997) Qualitative research articles: information for authors and peer reviewers. *Can Med Assoc J* **157**: 1442–6

Smith R (1997) Peer review: reform or revolution? Time to open up the black box of peer review. *Br Med J* **315**: 759–60

Smith R (1997) Opening up *BMJ* peer review: A beginning that should lead to complete transparency. *Br Med J* **318**: 4–5

Sweitzer BJ, Cullen DJ (1994) How well does a journal's peer review process function? A survey of authors' opinions. *JAMA* **272**: 152–3

Van Rooyen S, Godlee F, Evans S, Smith R, Black N (1998) Effect of blinding and unmasking on the quality of peer review: a randomised trial. *JAMA* **280**: 234–7

Van Rooyen S, Godlee F, Evans, Black N, Smith R (1999) Effect of open peer review on quality of reviews and on reviewers' recommendations: a randomised trial. *Br Med J* **318**: 23–7

7

Being a journal editor

Rebecca Linssen

Editing a journal can be a very difficult but very rewarding job. This chapter discusses the different areas that are involved in editing Hospital Medicine, to give readers an idea of the scope of the role.

Collins English Dictionary (1995) gives two core definitions of an editor:

A person who edits written material for publication, a person in overall charge of the editing and often the policy of a newspaper.

The role of editor of a journal varies widely between different journals. The editor's remit can include any or all of the following: selection of papers for inclusion, commissioning articles, promoting the journal, editing papers, overseeing production and printing, writing editorials and other articles. It also varies depending on the type of journal being edited — does it centre on reviews, does it publish original research, or does it mix both?

I edit *Hospital Medicine*, which is a clinical review journal, and so this chapter will focus mainly on the trials and tribulations involved in that role.

First priority: your readers

Your readers may vary in number from a few hundred to many hundreds of thousands, but you must always remember why they read the journal and try to tailor the content to their needs. It sounds obvious but it's the single most important thing for an editor to consider.

Hospital Medicine is a clinical review journal. Our aim is to provide our readers with concise, accurate, peer-reviewed clinical articles which allow them to update their knowledge with current thinking in whichever field they are interested in, without having to spend valuable time doing literature searches and hunting down articles in libraries. We publish fully referenced articles so that if a reader wants to gain further information on a subject, it is relatively easy for them to do so.

Authors

Commissioning, liaising with and advising authors is a major part of the editor's role. It is important to ensure that potential authors are fully briefed as to the exact requirements of commissioned articles, and that people who wish to submit articles to the journal are given appropriate encouragement.

An editor must recognise that articles are often a labour of love. While an author's enthusiasm about their article can be catching, it is often better to reject something on first discussion than to give false encouragement and then reject an inappropriate article at a later stage in the publishing process. The editor must be clear exactly what the article being discussed will entail and whether this will fit with the journal's style and content (see *Chapter 3*).

Authors can become very frustrated by the peer-review process, and the bulk of my monthly phone calls can be taken up by talking to them during this time. Most people who review papers are not paid for this work (see *Chapter 6*), primarily to reduce any possible bias to their reviews, and this can make it difficult to get papers looked at quickly. After authors have spent ages writing and editing their paper, they are often understandably keen to see it in print as soon as possible. This can be a problem if amendments to an article are required, as psychologically authors often feel that they have 'finished' with a paper when they have submitted it to a journal. It can be very difficult to regain the enthusiasm needed to work on a paper again, particularly if substantial changes are required. Tact and encouragement become very important at this stage. Being slightly more detached from the paper allows an editor to see how good it could be with a bit of attention, while authors are often so involved with the work that any amendments seem an insurmountable task.

Running the editorial team

The editor is often seen as the lynch pin of a journal, the point where everything comes together. The team of people involved in producing the editorial content of a journal is large and may include any or all of the following people:

- consultant editors
- editorial board members
- administrative team members
- authors, including professional authors and freelance writers
- production team
- printers
- copy editors

- designers
- illustrators.

These people all have different but vital roles to play in the production of a journal, from overseeing or undertaking peer review of articles, to laying-out and designing the journal, to editing the copy to ensure that it is accurate and that it reads well. I am often involved to varying degrees in all these processes, and have to maintain an overview of how they are all progressing.

Editing

With all the other areas to consider, it is easy to forget the actual title of the job: editor. Whether this involves subediting articles for sense and accuracy, or reading final corrected pages, the editor should have read the whole of an issue to ensure that the balance is correct, and that it is achieving all that it aims to do.

The subediting process can be complicated, particularly when working on journals that publish original research. It is very easy for authors to get so close to their own articles that they cannot see any mistakes or areas that are unclear. When I edit an article, I must look out for areas that readers might not understand, particularly important when working on a general journal like *Hospital Medicine*. It is easy for an author to assume a lot of prior knowledge that a specialist audience may have, but that doctors working in other fields may not. The editor's aim is to make the article as straightforward for people to read as possible without losing any accuracy. It's a fine line to tread.

Keeping up-to-date

Editors have to keep up-to-date with developments in the field, including scientific and pharmaceutical developments, political changes and educational issues. This ensures that journal content is topical, as well as potentially leading to changes in areas that the journal covers. An example of this within *Hospital Medicine* was the recognition that all doctors are becoming more involved in the education of other doctors. To this end, *Hospital Medicine* introduced the Education and Training Update section, which aims to help all hospital doctors in the day-to-day teaching that they have to do, covering issues such as management of trainees, educational issues and the theories behind educational methods.

Financial responsibilities

An awareness of commercial opportunities is important, particularly ensuring that potential activities do not compromise the journal's reputation or authority. This has to be balanced against the need for a journal to remain profitable in order for the publisher to continue to publish it. There are a number of potential areas of conflict involved in medical publishing, including advertisements which make unsubstantiated claims, the place of authors' conflicting/competing interests, supplements to the journal which may be sponsored by interested companies, and the place of advertorials. It is often the editor who establishes the journal's policy on each of the above areas, to ensure that readers can ascertain the validity of the information being presented to them.

It is important to remember that all journals must run within a set budget. Out of this pot come payments for authors, illustrators and freelance editors. It is part of the editor's role to balance all these payments, and get the best possible outcome with the budget available.

Representing the journal

The editor is often the public face of the journal. I represent the journal at press conferences, international meetings and interviews, and have to ensure that the journal is accurately portrayed on such occasions.

Why be an editor?

Editing is not always easy, and often requires large amounts of tact and diplomacy, as well as long hours and working to tight deadlines. However, most editors take inordinate pride in their journals and are extremely dedicated to their readers. The satisfaction which I feel when I see *Hospital Medicine* in print, or receive feedback from readers or authors, makes the whole juggling act worthwhile.

Key points

❀ The role of an editor can involve numerous different jobs, including commissioning, editing, writing and promoting the journal.

❀ The editor is vital in maintaining a balance between the interests and needs of different people involved in the journal.

❀ Editing is not always easy, but the satisfaction felt when seeing your journal in print makes it worthwhile.

Reference

Collins English Dictionary (1995) Harper Collins, London

8

The future of journals: where will electronic publishing take us?

Sally Morris

Journals provide much that is of immense value to the researcher and practitioner. Yet the economics of journals are unsustainable; the amount of publishable research is increasing more rapidly than the funds available to buy it. Various alternative models are emerging, none of them without problems. The way forward is not clear, but change is inevitable.

We can't go on like this

Researchers and publishers are locked in a vicious spiral which must, logically, end in the collapse of the journal system as we know it. The sheer quantity of research being carried out is increasing steadily; not because the number of papers per researcher has increased (it has in fact remained pretty constant; Tenopir and King, 2000), but simply because more than half of the researchers who have ever lived are alive, researching and writing today.

Publication in (preferably highly cited) peer-reviewed journals is crucial to a researcher's career progression, and indeed to the funding of his or her department (Association of Learned and Professional Society Publishers [ALPSP], 1999). As more research is done, more papers are written and eventually published somewhere (Lock, 1991). More papers being published must mean either the expansion of existing journals — thus increasing their cost — or the creation of new ones.

Either way, this places greater demands on library acquisition budgets. Yet the growth in research is not (and perhaps cannot be) accompanied by a corresponding increase in library funding (Mellon, 1992; National Science Foundation, 1997). Thus the sales per publication decline, which in turn pushes prices up if the publications are to remain financially viable. Higher prices mean even lower sales, and so on until the system finally breaks down.

Electronic publishing is not the solution

The advent of the World-Wide Web in the 1980s was hailed as the solution to this problem. Many of the players anticipated that electronic publication of journals would dramatically reduce costs, thus at least deferring the collapse of the system. Costs of paper, printing and postage would of course disappear, and the incremental cost of each additional sale would be close to zero.

Why have hopes of dramatic price cuts failed to materialise? It isn't as if publishers' profits have suddenly soared. There are a number of reasons why this solution turned out to be illusory:

❖ The costs which disappear with electronic publication are, for the majority of research journals (which these days have a circulation of under 1000 copies), a very small percentage of the total costs, about 4% for a 500-copy circulation (King and Tenopir, 1999). The proportions are, of course, different for large circulation journals, but many of these are at least partially supported by advertising, and advertisers' enthusiasm for the World-Wide Web has been somewhat muted.

❖ In addition, publishers have incurred various new costs, not only in getting content into appropriate electronic format, but also in creating and maintaining the systems which both mount it online and control access. What is more, the cost of selling journals, which was very low in the print world, has become a significant factor when complex licences have to be explained and negotiated; this, of course, adds to libraries' overhead costs too.

❖ The anticipated removal of restrictions on the number of pages which the publisher could afford to print, and thus the removal of publication delays, has not altogether materialised. It does become possible to publish articles as soon as they are available, rather than waiting for the publication date of the next journal issue. However, some of the resources (ie. people) required to process each article — the available referees to carry out peer review, the editor's time — are finite, while others — copy-editing, typesetting or its electronic equivalent — cannot be increased without increasing costs.

❖ Even when electronic versions are available, few libraries have had the confidence to drop the print-on-paper version altogether. The main reason is their justifiable concern about long-term accessibility — not just whether their licence will entitle them, without further cost, to continuing access to the material to which they subscribed in the past, but also whether anyone will be able to afford to preserve it so that it will be usable by tomorrow's technology.

Competitors to high-priced journals

One strategy which has been adopted by the SPARC initiative is to encourage the creation of new journals, whether or not electronic-only, which compete head-on with the most expensive existing journals, but are very significantly cheaper.[1] A number of journals have been launched under its auspices. However, it has not been without its critics. Some librarians complain that journals are not substitutable; in an ideal world, they would simply have to buy both the expensive journal and its competitor, thus stretching their available funds even thinner. Others have worked out that the cost per article in these new journals is in fact substantially higher; not surprising, given the difficulty of attracting authors to a new journal which has still to build its reputation (and impact factor). Publishers have found that, even with a certain number of guaranteed library sales, these titles — like all new journals these days — struggle to survive.

Alternative business models

One way or another, if readers (and authors) want journals more or less as we know them today, then those journals need to produce an adequate financial return for their publishers, whether these are not-for-profit or commercial. Journals which lose money will close, reducing the available outlets for publication. Creating more journals which are nevertheless sold on the existing pricing model — subscription or licence — may not be the answer. So, what about alternative models?

Site licences

Some publishers have introduced imaginative offers whereby a

1   SPARC (Scholarly Publishing and Resources Coalition) was set up by the
     US Association of Research Libraries. It is an alliance of libraries and
     other organisations which aims to foster more effective and cost-efficient
     systems of scholarly communication.

customer, or a group of customers (such as a consortium of libraries) can obtain electronic access to all the publisher's journals for little more than they previously spent on their print subscriptions to some of them. Libraries sometimes object that this model compels them to buy journals they don't want (although it's rarely the only available option). However, various publishers and other studies (Sanville, 2001; IDEAL) report that use of those journals which were previously not available to the library's users is remarkably high; this not only reduces the library's 'inter-library loan' expenditure, but also benefits the authors whose readership increases.

The problem is that the total cost still increases more steeply than the library budgets. If a library accepts such an offer from one publisher, it will probably have to cancel other subscriptions. And small publishers, such as learned societies, which may well have some of the journals of particular interest, cannot individually put together an appropriate 'package' of journals in this way. Initiatives are now under way to create 'consortia' of society and other smaller publishers to get round this problem.

Pay per view

An alternative way of buying journals is not by subscription (or licence) but 'by the drink', an article at a time. Publishers have argued that the price per article would have to be prohibitively high in order to keep journals financially viable, although of course without knowing the level of demand this is impossible to judge. Certainly it might be difficult to compete with the prices currently charged, by suppliers such as the British Library Document Supply Centre, for articles which are supplied under 'library privilege' (whereby no copyright fee is payable).

At the same time, librarians have argued that the resultant unpredictability of costs would be impossible to manage (although they seem to cope with electricity, photocopying and telephone bills on this basis). The preferred model (TECUP, 2000[2]; Ingenta, 2001) seems to be for subscription-like licences for 'core' journals, with pay-per-view availability for the rest. Who pays for the individual articles is of course a moot point; the library, the department or the user?

Author pays

A more radical approach to journal economics (Harnad, 1990, 1995) is to make the journal free to readers, and to cover the costs through submission and/or publication charges to authors. This is in some ways an extension of the 'page charges' model already in existence for a number of US journals (although less popular in other countries). This model has considerable attractions: not only does it make research articles equally available to all, regardless of their resources, it also scales with the increase in researchers and, thus, research articles (which library funds, as noted above, cannot possibly do).

It is difficult to judge how much the publisher would need to charge — some experiments (Haynes, 1999) have charged authors as little as $500, but it is not clear whether this is viable or not. Another difficulty is how the transition from one model to another would in fact be managed. Harnad argues that the savings from library budgets could be redirected towards paying these charges, but it is not obvious that universities and other organisations would actually be willing to do this. BioMed Central which has launched no fewer than sixty free journals, has also introduced a $500 author charge, but also an alternative

2   TECUP (Testbed Implementation of the European Copyright Users Platform) is an EU-funded project which analysed the feasibility of different mechanisms for the distribution, use and archiving of electronic products. Among other issues, it examined alternative licensing models.

whereby an institution can pay an amount, based on its size, which enables all its staff to submit papers free of charge. Those publishers who do make such charges usually waive them readily for authors who cannot pay, such as those based in less developed countries. This may not work outside science, however: while scientific research is generally expensive and grants are therefore fairly large, this is not the case in the arts and humanities and thus research funds are quite inadequate to cover publication costs.

One of the difficulties with the 'author (or funder) pays' model is the transitional period, in which authors have to choose between publishing in a (possibly highly cited) journal where they do not have to pay, but libraries do, and publishing in a new journal where they do have to pay but libraries and readers do not. An interesting 'half-way house' which might perhaps bridge the gap has been adopted by the journals of the Entomological Society of America. For 75% of the price of 100 offprints, the author can pay to make the online version of his or her article freely available to all; otherwise, it is only available to paying subscribers. The growing popularity of this approach with the journals' authors suggests that it may be a practical way forward (Walker, 2001a; Walker, 2001b)

Seizing control

Some see copyright ownership as the solution. Universities in the UK (like US universities before them) are flexing their muscles about their legal right to the copyright in their employees' work (Weedon, 2000). Authors, too, are increasingly keen to retain copyright in their own name rather than granting it to publishers. Interestingly, copyright ownership isn't really the point — it's what you do with it that matters. A growing number of publishers are perfectly happy for authors to reuse their own work in a wide variety of ways, often including mounting it on public websites; this can happen regardless of whether copyright is held by the author or the publisher (Morris, 2000).

In some disciplines, authors have for years placed their work in 'preprint' form in publicly accessible archives, such as the XXX physics preprint server. Stevan Harnad and others would argue that the solution to the 'journals crisis' is for all authors to place not just their preprints, but the final peer-reviewed and published version of their articles, in such databases (Harnad, 1990, 1995).

Standards and software are being developed to make these archives cross-searchable (Open Archives Initiative, http://www.openarchives.org). Similar initiatives are now being developed in medicine, with PubMed Central and its potential European counterpart E-BioSci (PubMed Central; E-BioSci). Recently, the Soros Foundation has put $3 million dollars into an initiative to extend these initiatives (Budapest Open Access Initiative). Perhaps curiously, neither Harnad's proposal nor that of PubMed Central see journals totally disappearing as a result, although their role would diminish to that of enablers and managers of peer review. Whether this would (a) preserve all the aspects of journals which authors and readers value (ALPSP, 2002) and (b) enable publishers (or their successors) to carry these out on a viable basis is unclear, however.

While publishers may not be able to find an economically viable way, at present, of making all their journal content freely available, a growing number are opening up their archival content. The Public Library of Science initiative (Public Library of Science) exhorted scientists to write, referee and edit only for those journals which made their back content freely available, in Open Archives, six months after publication. Although many thousands of scientists signed up, their actual behaviour didn't seem to change very much — they still wanted to be published in the 'best' journals. However, more and more publishers are, in fact, offering unrestricted access to their archival content, although the period after which it becomes free varies according to what the publisher believes it can afford (see list at http://www.freemedicaljournals.com). In addition, many publishers are participating in one or more of the burgeoning initiatives to make their electronic journal content freely (or very cheaply) available to readers in less developed countries (see list at http://www.library.yale.edu/~llicense/develop.shtml).

What happens to peer review?

One objection frequently raised to the idea of preprint databases is that the articles would not be subject to the quality control of peer review. This is not necessarily the case. The original PubMed Central proposal envisaged a panel of referees operating rather like the editorial boards of existing journals, although it is not clear whether they would be as motivated as they are when asked persuasively, by an editor whom they respect, to referee for an identifiable journal. E-print archives are expected to contain the final versions of articles after they have been peer-reviewed, edited and published — indeed, some publishers are even willing to provide the electronic files for this purpose.

However, peer review is not of course a single quality filter; articles are selected (or, more commonly, refined) for one journal rather than another on grounds not just of quality, but also of importance, novelty, appropriateness to the journal's topic, level of readership and so on. These distinctions make it possible for a reader to have a good idea what kind of articles to expect within the 'brand' of a particular journal.

This is not to say that the existing approach (or approaches, there is no gold standard of good practice) to peer review could not be improved. It has its critics (Lock, 1991; Jefferson and

Godlee, 1999) and there is interesting experimentation with alternative methods, for example soliciting (and in some cases publishing) open commentary (Electronic Transactions in Artificial Intelligence) either instead of or as well as traditional peer review. However, the scientific community does seem to set considerable store by some kind of quality control (Frankel *et al*, 2000; ALPSP, 1999; ALPSP, 2002).

Is medicine different?

The disciplines in which e-print archives have so far functioned particularly well tend to be highly focused, theoretical research areas within such subjects as physics, mathematics or computing. Research communities may perhaps be small enough for people to know each other's work from conferences, so that an author's name or affiliation tells them whether they will want to read his or her article.

Medicine, in common with a number of other subjects, has a relatively small number of active researchers in proportion to a very large number of practitioners. Practitioners want to know about the research that is most relevant to their work; but their time is precious, and they need this research to be identified, analysed and if possible distilled for them. They value 'meta-analyses' which show the overall conclusions of large numbers of related studies (ie. evidence-based medicine); they value summaries and review articles.

There is another problem which is particular to medicine. Quality control of medical information can be a matter of life and death. Not only unsound research, but simple typographical errors can be life-threatening. And even the best research information could be dangerously misunderstood by the casual reader. So it is necessary to maintain the safeguards of some form of quality control, and of identifying articles as being of a particular type (eg. specialist and technical rather than for the general reader). Journals as we know them do these things rather well.

What does the future hold?

Will journals as we know them exist at all in ten, twenty, fifty years' time? Some think not (Singer, 2000).

There is much that is highly valued in the way journals currently operate, in particular the quality control mechanism of peer review, but also the value added by good editing and presentation, and the convenience of collecting together articles within a journal brand. Whatever the future model, these strengths will need to be preserved in some way.

It seems rationally inevitable that the current business model must collapse — more and more research articles will be published, and there will not be enough additional funds to buy them. A new way of funding publication seems inevitable, and personally I think it makes good sense for the cost of publication to be seen as part of the cost of doing research.

An article might be deemed to be 'published' when it is made freely available on the author's own website (although readers would require assurances about its quality, version control, and permanence; Frankel *et al*, 2000). One can perhaps envisage 'journals' containing only abstracts, and linking directly, not only to the full text, but also to supporting data on the author's site.

As the sheer quantity of published research increases, tools for accessing that which is most relevant to the individual reader will become increasingly indispensable. I strongly suspect that this is not just a matter of 'smart' search engines which can learn what sort of articles you like and find 'more like that'. The role of human intelligence in finding, digesting and summarising that which is most relevant to a particular readership may become more, not less important as the potential information overload increases.

Thoughtful publishers have read the writing on the wall, and are already building online communities and information services which will offer tomorrow's readers tools for finding their way around the mass of available information, and making use of it to do their jobs better.

Key points

⌘ The current model of journal publishing is unsustainable.

⌘ Electronic publishing is not the panacea it was expected to be.

⌘ Various alternative models are being explored — one of the most hopeful seems to be 'author (or funding agency) pays'.

⌘ Publishers will need to concentrate on adding value to primary articles.

References

Association of Learned and Professional Society Publishers (1999) *What Authors Want*. ALPSP, Worthing

Association of Learned and Professional Society Publishers (2002) *Authors and Electronic Publishing*. ALPSP, Worthing

BioMed Central. See: http://www.biomedcentral.com

Budapest Open Access Initiative. See: http://www.soros.org/openaccess/

E-BioSci. See: http://www.embo.org

Electronic Transactions in Artificial Intelligence.
See: http://www.ida.liu.se/ext/etai

Frankel M, Elliott S, Blume M *et al* (2000) Defining and certifying
electronic publication in science. *Learned Publishing* **13**(4): 251–8
(free at: http://www.catchword.com/alpsp/09531513/v13n4/contp1-1.htm)

Harnad S (1990) Scholarly skywriting and the prepublication
continuum of scientific inquiry. *Psycholog Sci* **1**: 342–3; reprinted
in *Current Contents* **43**: 9–13
(free at: http://www.cogsci.soton.ac.uk/~harnad/Papers/
Harnad/harnad90.skywriting.html)

Harnad S (1995) Universal FTP archives for esoteric science and
scholarship: A subversive proposal. In: Okerson A, O'Donnell J,
eds. *Scholarly Journals at the Crossroads; A Subversive Proposal
for Electronic Publishing*. Association of Research Libraries,
Washington DC (available free at:
http://www.library.yale.edu/~okerson/subversive.html or
http://www.cogsci.soton.ac.uk/ ~harnad/subvert.html)

Haynes J (1999) New Journal of Physics: a web-based and
author-funded journal. *Learned Publishing* **12**(4): 265–9 (free at;
http://www.catchword.com/alpsp/09531513/v12n4/contp1-1.htm)

IDEAL. http://www.apnet.com/www/ideal/pressreleases/ustats.htm

Ingenta Institute (2001) *Assumptions versus Reality: User behaviour in
sourcing scholarly information*. Ingenta, Bath

Jefferson T, Godlee F (1999) *Peer Review in Health Sciences*. BMJ
Books, London

King DW, Tenopir C (1999) Evolving journal costs: implications for
publishers, libraries and readers. *Learned Publishing* **12**(4): 251–8
(free at: http://www.catchword.com/alpsp/09531513/v12n4/contp1-1.htm)

Lock S (1991) *A Difficult Balance*. BMJ Books, London

Mellon Foundation (1992) *University Libraries and Scholarly
Communication*. Association of Research Libraries, Washington DC

Morris S (2000) Authors and copyright. *Learned Publishing* **13**(2):
75–6
(free at: http://www.catchword.com/alpsp/ 09531513/v13n2/contp1-1.htm)

National Science Foundation (1997) *National Patterns of R&D Resources*. National Science Foundation, Arlington VA

Open Archives Initiative. See http://www.openarchives.org

PubMed. See: http://nih.gov/about/director/pubmedcentral/pubmedcentral.htm

Public Library of Science. See: http://www.publiclibraryofscience.org

Sanville T (2001) A method out of the madness: OhioLINK's collaborative responses to the serials crisis. *Serials* **14**(2)

Singer P (2000) Medical journals are dead: long live medical journals. *Can Med J* **162**(4): 517–8 (available at: http://www.cma.ca/cmaj/vol-162/issue-4/pdf/pg517.pdf)

SPARC. See: http://www.arl.org.sparc

TECUP (2000) *Draft Memorandum of Understanding*. TECUP, Goettingen (See http:// www.sub.uni-goettingen.de/gdz/tecup/ draftmou/pdf)

Tenopir C, King DW (2000) *Towards Electronic Journals: Realities for scientists, librarians and publishers*. Special Libraries Association, Washington DC

Walker TJ *Authors willing to pay for instant web access*. Nature Web Debates. Available at: http://www.nature.com/nature/debates/e-access/Articles/walker.html

Walker TJ (2001) Market-driven free access to journal articles. *The Scientist* **15**(43) also available free at: http://www.the-scientist.com/yr2001/jun/opin010611.html

Weedon R (2000) *Policy Approaches to Copyright in Higher Education Institutions*. University of Strathclyde, Glasgow

9

Writing for the popular press: to inform and entertain

Carol Cooper

Many doctors write for consumer publications. Even more would like the chance to do so. This chapter explains how to bridge the gap between writing scientific papers and writing for the popular press, and offers realistic guidance on how to find a way into this competitive market.

Why write for the popular press

Samuel Johnson said: 'No man but a blockhead ever wrote, except for money'. Writing for the papers can be lucrative, but in reality there are few doctors who make a comfortable living solely from writing. The thrill of seeing your name in print on the news-stands usually exceeds the thrill of seeing your name on the cheque.

One rewarding aspect of writing is that you can communicate with many more people than you can even in the busiest outpatient clinic. Patients attending your clinic may read your articles too, and it can be amusing to hear patients quote your wise words on irritable bowel syndrome (usually incorrectly).

Writing is also something interesting to include in your CV. Whether the appointments panel approves of the *Sunday Mirror* or not, you can bet it will attract comment.

These reasons alone, however, are not enough. You should only write for the press if you really enjoy it. As with all extra-curricular activities, it is time-consuming. It can also be inconvenient. Are you prepared to forgo an evening with the children to scribble frantically for a 9.00 pm deadline? Are you still happy to do it when you know your efforts will end up forgotten in cat litter trays?

How to write

Medics have a huge advantage in writing on health; they know the subject already, which means that they can often produce a good piece quickly without having to look anything up. Fields with an obvious advantage to the papers are paediatrics, psychiatry, general practice, obstetrics and gynaecology, but the human body is endlessly fascinating and few branches of medicine or surgery are totally devoid of interest to lay readers.

On the whole, doctors are intelligent, and some are good communicators. A few even write very well. Even so, a lot of good writers do not succeed in writing well for the popular press.

One difficulty is that medics sometimes know their subject too well, and forget that a layman or woman may find the same facts hard going. Writing is easy if you bear in mind that people read papers and magazines for entertainment. Whatever you write has to be easy and fun to read. If you want to expound your latest theory, a lecture at the Royal College of Physicians might be more appropriate than the pages of a tabloid.

All of us tend subconsciously to mirror the style of the material we read. If you are heavily into Proust, your writing may not appeal much to the *Daily Mail*. Pore over Proust if you must, but also spend time reading the publication you are aiming at.

Once you put pen to paper or fingers to keyboard, bear in mind that your first sentence is your most important. Aim to grab the reader's attention in ten words or less (some say three words, but they probably have the *Daily Sport* in mind). You may not decide on your first sentence until you have written most of the piece, but spend some time on it. The opening few words have to be strong enough to lure the reader away from doing anything other than read the rest of your article. 'Your mobile phone could make you infertile' would be an arresting opener. If it were true, it would be even better.

A word about headlines, the editor or sub-editor chooses these, not the author of the feature. By all means give your article a title that reflects its content, but it is pointless spending hours thinking up something witty because it will probably be changed.

Keep all your sentences short and clear. Some writers pitch their features to appeal to an intelligent fourteen-year-old, but in doing so try not to patronise. You are aiming to entertain and inform (so-called 'infotain') readers, not show them up.

Working out the Gunning fog index (Gunning, 1971) can help keep things accessible. Take 100 words of your article and count the number of sentences within them, then calculate the average sentence length. Add this to the number of complex words (usually taken to be three syllables or longer) within your 100-word passage. Multiply this by 0.4, which gives the fog index. The lower the fog index, the clearer the writing. As a rough guide, tabloids usually score between eight and ten, more serious newspapers average twelve to fourteen, and many medical journals have a fog index of fourteen to sixteen. Really abstruse publications will easily exceed sixteen. (While *Hospital Medicine* usually scores about thirteen, the fog index of this chapter is around nine.)

If you can't be bothered with Gunning's calculation, just look at your sentence length and try to keep each one well under thirty words.

Table 9.1: Style in a nutshell

By all means start sentences with conjunctions. But stay out of these traps:

- Try to avoid passive verbs and constructions. If these are used, it is suspected that life could be sapped from your writing.

- Leave out redundant phrases and any other expressions that add little or nothing to the meaning you are trying to impart.

- Remember to always delete split infinitives.

- Banish footnotes. They are usually useless.

- Avoid clichés like the plague.

- Never drop names, as Somerset Maugham was wont to say.

- Steer clear of foreign words. Editors think they're *de trop*. (Like this one.)

On being a true professional

As a doctor, you must stick to General Medical Council (GMC) guidelines (GMC, 1995). Those who write for lay readers must never purport to be the best in their field (even if they are). Always make it clear that you cannot see patients as a result of anything you have written. There is more GMC advice on writing and broadcasting, but at this point I would like to add a humane consideration: do not tell every reader to see his GP without delay.

Be professional in your dealings with editors and respect deadlines. An aortic aneurysm may well have kept you away from the word processor, but the editor cannot go to press with a blank page. And deadlines can be very tight. I well recall the tabloid features editor who wanted me to produce a 600-word piece on exercise and reassured me with: 'Don't worry, you've got bags of time. Forty minutes, if you need it'.

Accept changes. The sub-editor who deletes the odd comma or adjective is not an infanticidal maniac flourishing a knife at your babies. You can avoid errors creeping in at the sub-editing stage if you are faxed a copy of the final page proof before it goes to press. There isn't always time in the publishing schedule to allow this, but you can ask.

Breaking into the market

This is the hardest part because it takes luck as well as talent and perseverance. If you can arrange to be famous first, editors will beat a path to your door. Most of us are less fortunate and have to make our own way in. The best way to approach an editor is still by letter (rather than fax or e-mail) with a few words about yourself and an idea or two for articles.

Sometimes a sycophantic letter does the trick. ('I always enjoy reading *Baby's Bottom Monthly*, but I notice you do not have a paediatrician advising readers on thrush in the nappy area.') Enclose copies of some of the articles you have published. Sadly, 'Simultaneous turnover of normal and dysfunctional C1 inhibitor as a probe of in vivo activation of C1 and contact-activatable proteases' (Woo *et al*, 1985) may not help your cause. If you have not already written for lay readers, you can build up a useful portfolio by writing first for some of the softer publications, such as the freebies you and your colleagues receive, or for newspapers aimed at GPs or nurses. Fillers for the *British Medical Journal* can also be a good starting-point.

Getting the right idea may seem daunting but does not have to be. Just think of a topic which might appeal to readers of that paper. I cannot stress strongly enough that you must study the publication in detail first. It may not matter if the editor rejects your idea — if he/she likes the sound of you, he/she may commission you to write on a different subject.

Consider joining the Medical Journalists' Association (see *p. 80*). This is the national organisation for people who write on health and medicine and organises a number of events and seminars. It will help you meet other writers and get known. Most doctors who write qualify for affiliate rather than full membership. However, this still gets them into the directory of members and onto the list of freelances, which can be a rich source of new work.

Once you have got your first commission for the popular press, you are nearly there. Establish what you will be paid for a piece, but do not be fussy about rates. When you are better known, you can afford to tell the editor laughingly: 'You jest. That's the kind of money I used to write for ten years ago.'

Key points

- ✳ Writing for the popular press is time-consuming but can be fun for the writer and informative for readers.

- ✳ Whatever your topic, the article has to be entertaining.

- ✳ You may need to re-examine your notion of a good writing style.

- ✳ One can still be a real professional, both as a doctor and as a tabloid hack.

- ✳ Getting ideas into print requires strategy and hard work.

- ✳ There is no substitute for in-depth study of your target publications.

References

General Medical Council (1995) *Advertising — Guidance from the GMC*. GMC, London

Gunning R (1971) *The Technique of Clear Writing*. McGraw-Hill, Boston

Woo P, Lachmann P, Harrison R, Amos N, Cooper C (1985) Simultaneous turnover of normal and dysfunctional C1 inhibitor as a probe of in vivo activation of C1 and contact-activatable proteases. *Clin Exp Immunol* **61**: 1–8

Further reading

Albert T (2000) *The A to Z of Medical Writing*. BMJ Books, London

Strunk W, White EB (2000) *The Elements of Style*. 4th edn. Allyn & Bacon, Boston

Useful address

Philippa Pigache, Hon secretary
Medical Journalists' Association
5 St James' Road
Tunbridge Wells
Kent TN1 2JY
Tel: 01892 515857
e-mail: pigache@globalnet.co.uk

10

How to write a critical letter and respond to one

Neville W Goodman

Critical letters are important. They correct the published record. To write a critical letter requires tact; to respond to one requires tact — and the humility that comes with the realisation that belief in an observation or an idea does not make it true.

Why and how you should write your letter

Twenty years ago, Professor Sam Shuster (1981) remarked that published work was accorded almost biblical reverence. Reviewing books based on conference proceedings, he complained that too many reviewers were uncritical to the point of mere regurgitation.

Doctors all know that journals use peer review to assess articles submitted for publication, but perhaps not all doctors know much about the process (see *Chapter 6*). Some journals use just one or two referees for each paper; others use a panel of referees with knowledge of different aspects of research, eg. statistics. Particularly in the more specialist journals, published research may have been approved after little more than a perfunctory scan for significant phrases by a referee during a convenient train journey.

A referee may just decide they like the message of the paper, without carefully assessing the methods. A referee may be unfamiliar with all aspects of the study, or may be uncomfortable with statistics. Unless the authors cite suspiciously few recent papers, a referee is unlikely to check the literature for important omissions. Unless a referee is a truly deeply read expert, relevant papers published long ago can easily be omitted.

All of these errors need correction, and a journal's readers can do this. And even if a paper has been properly and thoroughly reviewed, there may be differences of opinion that are not brought out in the discussion. All scientific journals worthy of the name should publish readers' comments (Maddox, 1990a; Bhopal and Tonks, 1994), which one editor has described as 'the proper dialogue of science' (Horton, 1995).

Writing a letter is no different from writing anything else: plan, then write. First decide the important error or mis-interpretation and describe it succinctly. Then explain why it is an error, giving references if appropriate. Do not fall into the trap of yourself failing to cite a previously published similar criticism. Finally, explain clearly and simply what the authors should have done or written. And leave it at that. Draw the threads together into the coherent letter, which should be as short as possible. Pithy one-liners make the best letters in newspapers; the same is true in medical journals. Short letters are much more likely to be read, because they stand out on the page.

Writing letters is a good way to hone general writing skills (Goodman and Edwards, 1997). In summary, use (don't employ) short words in short sentences, and make every word count (not make a positive impact). Impress with fact, not false erudition.

Do not start your letter with, 'I read with interest the article by Smith and co-workers...' but with your main point. Consider making your criticism less personal by referring indirectly to the authors rather than directly by their names. If you want to make it more personal, you can soften the blow with, 'Smith and co-workers make the common error of...' rather than the bald 'Smith and co-workers should have...'.

Do not use deliberately provocative language without extremely good reason. In my view that should be only for accusations of serious research malpractice, not just for minor misdemeanours or misinterpretations (although strict definition of where the one merges into the other has defied many committees for many years).

Having written your letter, put it in a drawer for a couple of days: I do not recommend dashing off critical letters without second thoughts. Show your letter to a colleague before posting it.

Whatever the tone of your letter, you will need to write an accompanying letter to the editor of the journal, explaining why he or she should publish your criticism. There is no need to be repetitive, so 'I enclose a letter commenting on some aspects of a study published in...' may be enough, although it may be worth adding at least one explanatory sentence to avoid immediate editorial 'triage' (see *Chapter 3*). The more critical and accusatory your letter, the more explanation you need to give the editor, who may anyway ask you — or later take an editorial decision — to tone down your sentiments.

If the editor thinks your letter is worth publishing, it will usually be sent to the original authors to allow them to comment. It is unusual for letters to receive any other peer review; indeed, letters are 'post-publication peer review' (Caswell, 1992; Shahar, 1997; Winker and Fontanarosa, 1999). I usually send a copy of the critical letter directly to the authors as well; that way, you may get an answer to your criticisms, even if not the satisfaction (and reward) of seeing them in print. Do not be too hopeful: in my experience, letters of congratulation for a study well done or an article well thought-out almost always receive replies, but criticisms do not.

Responding to criticism

You are unlikely to be shown the authors' response to your letter, but it is unlikely to be satisfactory or complimentary. Anyone who writes a lot of critical letters needs to have a thick skin. With honourable exceptions, authors do not look on criticism as a light to the truth, humbly saying 'Thank you'. Criticism is a challenge to be overcome, usually by a mixture of semantic wrigglings, ignoring the main point but expansively countering less important ones (a practical reason for keeping critical letters succinct and accurate), and sometimes by being implicitly abusive (Goodman, 1996). Maddox (1990b) wrote that even if there is no option but to admit error it is rarely done, and authors may resort to blaming a third party whose work they relied on. While those in the field often know full well what is going on, casual readers cannot.

Sometimes authors are explicitly abusive, for some reason, particularly after criticism of English. Norman (1977) criticised the use of the word 'aggressive', as in 'the aggressive control of pain'. In his reply Chaney ignored Norman's point completely, accused him of being obsessed with semantics, and added snidely, 'However, constructive criticism and comments regarding study design, data analysis, and clinical implications are always welcome' — a moot point. To the editor's credit, a later letter was published suggesting that, 'Chaney should have had the courtesy to defend his use of the word' (Goodman, 1998). There was no published response from Chaney.

Some journals do not send letters to the original authors for comments, which I consider unreasonable if the letter is critical; authors must be given the chance to defend themselves. Once, when such a letter appeared some weeks after a paper of mine, the journal refused to publish my rebuttal on the grounds that it would be too long after publication of my original paper — which was entirely the journal's doing.

Whether you are criticised by a letter forwarded to you or an unheralded letter in a journal, the first response should be to take a deep breath. Re-read the criticism dispassionately. Show it to a colleague. If your critic is correct, have the grace to say so, with gratitude; add an excuse or reason for your error if you wish, but keep the error your own. If the criticism is unfounded, your written response should simply counter the presented facts. Make no comments on the motives or character of your critic, and resist the urge to dig up some dirt on them — dirt will make you feel better, but it may stick to you.

The effect of your letter

The first effect is that you have a publication for your CV. Traditionally, letters carry little weight compared with more 'substantial' publications, but canny interviewers realise that letters can say a lot about the writer that won't necessarily be apparent in a research publication, particularly one which has many authors. Letters are also easy to find and quick to read.

Comments on published work are indexed (if not perfectly or completely) in databases: there is a comment field in Medline, although the searcher has actively to retrieve the comment. This allows relevant critical comments to be cited along with the primary research. This happens less than it should: when Bhopal and Tonks (1994) drew attention to it they cited an earlier paper from 1955, and elicited a comment (Kalla, 1994) reporting a journal editor's admission that it was not normal practice to cite correspondence in editorials. Even papers retracted because of outright fraud are still being cited (Campanario, 2000).

None of this should stop you writing a letter; almost certainly, not enough of us do (Caswell, 1992). Your comment, correction or interpretation will not be cited if unmade and you cannot then complain if subsequent authors make the same mistake or repeat it.

The future of the critical letter

E-mailed comments about published articles appear in the online *British Medical Journal* (http://www.bmj.com) within twenty-four to forty-eight hours, with little editorial interference. Other journals may follow. In some ways this is good: authors receive and can respond to criticism quickly. People who would otherwise not get round to typing and posting a letter can send an instant (of which: beware!) e-response. Those with a direct interest in a topic can follow the debate. The reward is less clear. All *BMJ* e-letters are considered for publication in the paper journal, although the acceptance rate is decreasing; but is an e-letter a publication? There is little editorial control, and there are 'professional' e-letter writers. Controversial articles can attract rambling, illogical and repetitive axe-grinding dialogue: is one obliged to search through this stuff and then have to cite it? The future of the critical letter depends on the future of medical publishing and the rewards that authors obtain from it. The only thing certain about the future is that we do not know what is going to happen. For the moment, if the thought strikes you, write about it.

Key points

- ⌘ Critical letters are an important scientific source.

- ⌘ Write your letter clearly and simply.

- ⌘ Do not be hasty.

- ⌘ Explain briefly to the editor why your criticism matters and send a copy to the authors you are criticising.

- ⌘ Be prepared to accept criticism if it is warranted.

- ⌘ Do not be abusive — implicitly or explicitly.

- ⌘ Published letters are an easily accessed part of your CV, and are indexed in Medline with the original article.

- ⌘ E-responses may be the future of 'post- publication peer review'.

References

Bhopal RS, Tonks A (1994) The role of letters in reviewing research. *Br Med J* **308**: 1582–3

Campanario JM (2000) Fraud: retracted articles are still being cited. *Nature* **408**: 288

Caswell A (1992) Letters to the editor. An audit of the MJA's correspondence columns. *Med J Aust* **157**: 63–4

Goodman NW (1996) Revising the research record (letter). *Lancet* **347**: 474

Goodman NW (1998) Neither obsession nor distraction: words must be chosen well (letter). *Anesth Analg* **87**: 743–4

Goodman NW, Edwards ME (1997) *Medical Writing: a Prescription for Clarity*. Cambridge University Press, Cambridge

Horton R (1995) Revising the research record. *Lancet* **346**: 1610–1

Kalla G (1994) The role of letters in reviewing research. *Br Med J* **309**: 539

Maddox J (1990a) Saying sorry but not sorry. *Nature* **343**: 589

Maddox J (1990b) Should camp-followers be policemen? *Nature* **348**: 107

Norman J (1997) Should we be aggressive anaesthesiologists? (With response from Chaney MA) (letter). *Anesth Analg* **85**: 706–7

Shahar E (1997) Your letter failed to win a place... (with response from Smith R, Crossan E). *Br Med J* **315**: 1608–9

Shuster S (1981) Autumn books. Loneliness of a long distanced reviewer. *Br Med J* **283**: 1443–4

Winker MA, Fontanarosa PB (1999) Letters: a forum for scientific discourse. *JAMA* **281**: 1543

11

Producing a multimedia CD-ROM

Mira Vogel, Gerry CJ Bennett

*The multimedia capabilities of modern computers
promise a rich contribution to medical education,
integrating video, animation and graphics as a single
courseware package. Using the new generation of design
tools, computer-assisted learning material can be
successfully created in-house.*

Introduction

For the medical learner/user, gaining familiarity with fundamental
procedures and mechanisms is compromised by restrictions on
time, location and resources. Although the potential of modern
computers to provide alternatives has long been recognised,
widespread problems have still to be addressed (Greenhalgh,
2001). A good piece of education software is the tip of a large
iceberg, the invisible part comprising needs assessment, design,
knowledge validation, implementation, evaluation and maintenance.
The CD-ROM project ongoing at Barts and the Royal London
Hospital aims to fulfil and surpass the requirements of students of
geriatric medicine. This chapter will discuss the process of
developing a computer-based educational package, using the
CD-ROM project as a case study (*Step 1*).

Step 1

The CD-ROM project was conceived with several factors in mind. Electronic vehicles for information are increasingly widespread and knowledge has ceased to be the preserve of the university, which 'no longer provides the guiding dictum to knowledge, nor controls the direction that a client may choose to traverse' (Abeles, 1999). Moreover, students now pay for their higher education and consequently are developing an awareness of their consumer rights. These rights include access to knowledge which is accessible, validated, well structured, current and transparent in its sources.

Medical students are likely to perceive (and have often been constrained to perceive) their task as that of learning large amounts of facts by rote to regurgitate at exam time. They are consequently under great pressure to abandon an effective, deep, elaborative approach to learning in favour of a superficial approach which commits vast amounts of isolated facts to memory, with poor rates of retention (Coles, 1998). Although problem-based learning addresses this issue, medical students still need support to make their learning experience an active, connected, elaborative process rather than a passive one.

The suite of CD-ROM study guides which will be the outcome of this project aims to offer the 'facts', substantiated by references and reinforced by examples, tests and games. A drill-down approach to knowledge has been adopted, and users who wish to do so will be able to access layers of information in increasing detail. The package will be available over the school Intranet and in CD-ROM format.

Before starting

The developer should be acquainted with the resources at their disposal, in particular constraints on time and money. In designing learning technology, it is a general principle that users, both direct (students) and indirect (tutors, assessors) should be involved throughout.

Project management software can be extremely useful in devising a programme for large or complex projects, and when the (inevitable) pitfalls and delays occur, the burden of restructuring is considerably lessened.

Evaluators should be identified and approached. Approval for the study, if required, can take months to obtain, and applications should be made early.

After attending to these preliminary considerations (*Step 2*), the user can begin the needs-assessment phase.

Step 2

A management committee, including clinical, financial, educational and student representatives, was convened at the beginning of the project. Monthly meetings were arranged to discuss progress and future direction of the project. The local ethics committee was approached with a methodology for evaluation.

Before acquiring project management software, a programme was drawn up on a spreadsheet. The actual course of the project was subsequently recorded over time in a separate workbook as a comparison to the original programme.

Needs assessment

To ensure that precious resources are not squandered, it is necessary to establish the user requirements for effective learning and whether computer-assisted learning (CAL) is appropriate in the given domain. This information is crucial to design of the CAL.

Why computer-assisted learning?

So what is wrong with traditional paper-based notes or personal tuition? Nothing, but different media have distinct features, as detailed in *Table 11.1*.

Table 11.1: Comparison of features of three different learning media

Features	Paper-based	Personal	Computer-based
Portable	✓	✗	(✓)
Interactive	✗	(✓)	✓
Multimedia	(✓)	(✓)	✓
Self-paced	✓	✗	✓
Self-directed	✓	✗	✓
Searchable	(✓)	(✓)	✓
Non-linear	✗	✗	✓
No aptitude required	✓	✓	✗
Query potential	✗	✓	✗

✗=no; ✓=yes; (✓)=limited

The uptake of computers both in the home and in the workplace has created a climate conducive to computer-aided learning (IT for All, 1999), should it be required. CAL is likely to be useful in situations where:

- target users have demonstrated aptitude with IT
- restrictions exist on traditional communication media
- the knowledge base changes rapidly
- learners/users operate at different paces
- learners/users have diverse needs
- learners/users are based in diverse locations.

If a need for CAL is established, the second phase of needs assessment — requirements gathering — can begin (*Step 3*).

Requirements gathering

Requirements can be considered in three categories (Preece *et al*, 1994):

❖ Functional requirements specify what the joint system of the human and the computer must achieve.
❖ Data requirements specify the structure and data required.
❖ Usability requirements formulate targets for user performance and satisfaction.

At this early stage, ambiguity, omissions or unfeasible requirements should be brought to the fore. The developer may have to use several techniques to expose these, including interviews, observation and surveys. Basic prototypes of the end product are useful at this stage, stimulating the imagination and providing an anchor for speculation (*Step 4*).

After requirements have been identified, the project moves into the design phase.

Step 3

Students of geriatric medicine in the school study a large number of subjects in a short period of time. Needs were identified for:

- material to supplement modules restricted by lack of staff, time and money
- a more interactive element to enliven the 'drier' material
- different strata of detail
- easily maintainable and updateable material.

Consequently, the aims of the CD-ROM project were:

- to signpost and deliver access to information in more detail for motivated students
- to make the learning experience involved and active
- to maximise resources
- to facilitate maintenance of the knowledge.

The study guides are intended to provide an extra learning media in line with advances in technology and extend student learning options.

Design

There are three main threads to the design phase:

- ❖ Layout design, concerned with the interface — the way users will interact with the knowledge.
- ❖ Physical design, the architecture or structure of the CAL project. This is how the information is physically stored and affects the way in which it can be accessed by users and maintained by developers.
- ❖ Knowledge structure: the order and manner of presenting the knowledge.

Step 4

Two hundred and two fourth-year medical students have completed a needs-assessment questionnaire which explored perception of IT ability, attitudes towards learning with computers, access to a computer, and attitudes to learning about health care of older people. The response indicated that students were satisfied with the platform for CAL. Seventy-one per cent reported that they would find a computer package covering core areas of the course and supplementary material useful or very useful. Thirty-two per cent of respondents considered themselves competent or advanced in terms of ability with computers, while the remainder reported as intermediate (37%), novice (24%) or complete beginner (5%). Sixty-five per cent had a computer, while fifty-one per cent had Internet access. Sixty-eight per cent were not interested or not particularly interested in health care of older people, and this correlated with initial take-up of the package.

Layout design

Layout design is concerned with the interface between user and content. Users expect to be able to manipulate knowledge directly and intuitively, based on:

- assimilated knowledge of the outside world
- conventions established within the package itself.

For this reason, any metaphor which is used in the interface should be consistent with the culture of the target user and internally consistent throughout the CAL package. For example, the question mark icon, which is used throughout the guide to denote study guide questions, is intuitive to most Western users. Revision is a harder concept to depict. The spectacles icon, although less intuitive, exploits the 'vision' of 'revision'.

Designers of new software tend to take advantage of these established conventions. Where icons are more obscure, it is particularly important to use them consistently and exclusively throughout the guide to signal the same type of information.

At the design stage, the ergonomics of the interface should be considered. Some key points to consider are (Dix *et al*, 1993):

- a negative contrast (dark colours on a light screen) provides higher luminance and increased readability
- approximately 8% of males and 1% of females are colour blind
- visual symbols are easier to process than text and can also relieve a monotonous screen of text
- lines of text should be between 58 and 132mm in length
- word shape clues should be preserved by using a clear, lower-case font.

It is a good idea to solicit feedback while developing the interface, since it is often inconvenient to make changes at a later stage.

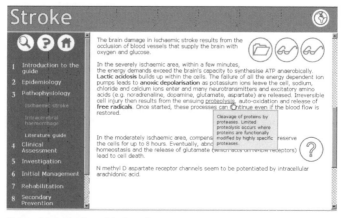

Figure 11.1: Study guide interface

Physical design

This is the architecture or structure of the CAL package; how it has been programmed to store and present the knowledge that it contains (*Step 5*). All computer systems should use an architecture that is:

- extendable: it should be easy to append seamlessly extra material
- maintainable and updateable: it should be easy to implement changes.

Today's prevalent interactive computing environment is known as WIMP because it uses windows, icons, menus and pointers. A user opens an application in a window, which can be resized, minimised or closed. Interaction with this window and its content is achieved through icons and menus. Icons are pictorial representations of objects and concepts (*Figure 11.2*), which are more easily processed than text. They are often realistic but can also be highly stylised, involving lateral thinking or puns.

Menus offer visual reminders about choices of operations. They can pull down, pop up or remain constantly visible. A menu choice is selected using the last component of the WIMP interface — the pointer. The pointer, traditionally an arrow, is controlled with an input device, such as a mouse or trackball. In the quest for the intuitive interface, pointers are beginning to give way to technology like touch screens and mouse pens. Advances in artificial intelligence have harnessed brain wave fluctuations to control an external environment with the power of thought (Lusted and Knapp, 1996).

Step 5

The design of the study guide interface (*Figure 11.2*) incorporates a sidebar menu (or table of contents) in a separate frame. This means that the menu remains visible at all times. The menu contains three icons for access to search, home (the navigational hub of the guide) and help pages, including a user manual. The menu situated below these icons is arranged as a hierarchical tree menu, a well-established convention, an example of which can be found in Microsoft's file management program Windows Explorer. The menu can be expanded or contracted to show or hide sub-sections. Each menu item is a hyperlink, which signals its interactivity by changing its appearance when the mouse pointer is passed over it. Clicking on a menu item instantly loads the section with which the hyperlink is associated, replacing what was previously on screen. Hypertext is intended to allow navigation through different sections in a non-linear way with a minimum number of mouse clicks.

A decision was taken to prioritise usability over appearance, which resulted in sacrificing some design control over the position of elements on the screen. Different users with different specifications and settings for their machines can have very different experiences of the same site. For example, screen size can vary by several inches, and this must be considered when specifying the size of components, such as graphics and text. Where possible, sizes within the interface have been specified in relative terms, allowing the user freedom to adjust different elements to suit his or her eyesight or screen size. The three frames which make up each page can be resized by clicking and dragging their borders, while most web browsers allow users to specify the size of the text, assuming the designer has not disabled this option.

Images, used extensively to provide easily processed visual clues, are problematic because they cannot be resized. However, while hovering on these images, a label appears. The template for the site has been designed according to guidelines from the W3C Web Accessibility Initiative (WAI, 2002) and is accessible to browsers for the blind or partially sighted. A number of tools are available to help developers to check the accessibility of sites, including Bobby (Cast, 2000) and WAVE. These check submitted source code for elements which could stymie alternative browsers, and offer advice to rectify problems.

The knowledge in the guide is arranged in pages that can be navigated using the menu, the map or the search engine. Clickable icons, appearing to the right of the top-level information, signal where users can drill down for extra knowledge. Different icons denote different types of knowledge ('revision' and 'valuable information' are shown in *Figure 11.2*). Questions, indicated by the question mark icon, are also signalled throughout the guides. Users also have instantaneous access to glossary definitions by pointing the mouse pointer over coloured words.

Figure 11.2: Icons (Icon Bazaar, 2001)

Knowledge structure

Knowledge should be structured appropriately by experts. It is important to consider future maintenance during this process. Human memory is notoriously unreliable, and the original developer will not necessarily carry out future maintenance. For this reason, it is important to document the structure of the knowledge. Concept maps, such as the one in *Figure 11.3*, are one way of representing knowledge structures.

With this method, it is possible to drill down, generating further maps, until one can account for the entire content.

Knowledge validation

As medical knowledge expands, existing bodies of knowledge require rigorous maintenance. The developer should be satisfied that the material is current, complete and accurate (*Step 6*).

At this stage, copyright and confidentiality issues should be resolved.

Multimedia material

Well-produced multimedia material, using sound and moving images, in medical education is far richer learning material than text or static images alone. Its production is highly technical; awareness of a range of issues, from the importance of file sizes to how the multimedia material can be integrated, is crucial.

Producing multimedia material is also time-consuming and expensive. For this reason, developers must examine the relative merits of outsourcing and in-house production. Out-sourced multimedia is usually high quality, stylish, reliable and expensive. The professionals involved in its production usually have a good awareness of technical issues. However, there are disadvantages to outsourcing, including a potential loss of control of the final product and its minutiae. On the other hand, producing multimedia in-house involves a large initial investment in terms of money and in terms of time spent practising with hardware and software. It also involves a continuing investment of time spent recording and editing the product.

However, in-house developers bring expertise and awareness of subtleties of the subject matter which rarely exist outside. Additionally, the process of planning, scheduling and recording can be less protracted where the multimedia developer is on site.

Whether in-house or outsourced, a planning stage is necessary for animation, video and audio recording. In common with film-making, this usually involves 'storyboarding', the process which includes accounting for each 'take' and outlining changes of focus or camera angle. If a scenario with human contributors is planned, it is necessary to script and rehearse any dialogue and activity.

The type of file format selected for the material affects how the user can access the multimedia. For example, where animations have been developed using certain tools, the user requires a separate programme (known as a plug-in) to view the animation. This could be included with the CAL package, but the user may resent having to install it. In some circumstances, multimedia files can also 'stand alone' without needing to be interpreted by a separate programme and this is the most desirable scenario.

Although time-consuming and expensive to produce, well-executed multimedia material is extremely engaging and offers a real opportunity for self-paced, self-directed learning without the traditional restrictions of time and space. In this respect, it undeniably asserts the worth of CAL.

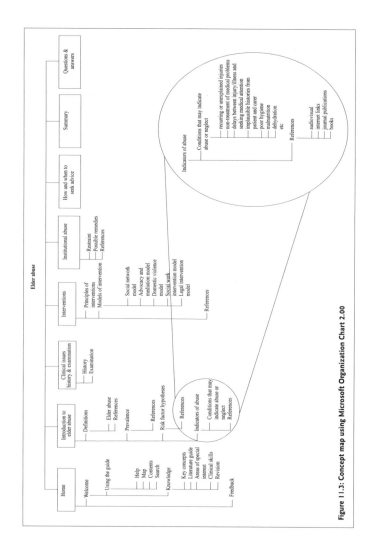

Figure 11.3: Concept map using Microsoft Organization Chart 2.00

Step 6

The expert authors of the original study guides are extremely busy and dispersed between Belfast and London. It was therefore necessary to streamline the knowledge validation process as far as possible, and to this end a meeting with each author was arranged to discuss their vision for implementing the guide and to hand out a pack containing:

- a prototype CAL version of their study guide on CD-ROM
- their original paper-based guide
- a copy of the guide on floppy disk
- guidelines for review and amendment.

A prototype of the CAL package is included to stimulate interest and imagination. It is suggested that the paper guide be used for review and changes or extra material be inserted in red font on the digital document using a word processing package. Additionally, a deadline for validation is negotiated at the time of handing out the review pack so that the project programme can be adjusted accordingly. Authors are asked to suggest a best-before date for the next review, which should reflect the pace of change in their domain.

Tools for implementation

The CD-ROM is a well-established medium with a large data capacity. CD-ROM drives are available in the vast majority of computers purchased in the last five years, an advantage which, at the time of writing, is not true of other digital distribution media. Some hybrid media have successfully integrated CD-ROM with network technology. Mattheos *et al* (2000) achieved a seamless package using video material on CD-ROM to compensate for slow connection speeds over a network. Consequently, they preserved the ease of update, low costs and 'scalability' offered by networks, and at the same time were able to overcome specific problems which their network experienced with large files.

The choice of authoring tool depends on the content and intended use of the end product. Demonstration versions of many tools are available free for download over the Internet and can be sampled before purchase. It is often difficult to evaluate the relative merits of several options, and one way of overcoming this is to prototype rapidly a representative part of the CAL package using the shortlisted tools. The most appropriate development tool should then emerge from this process.

As well as providing a convenient environment for development (*Step 7*), the selected tool should be capable of rendering an end product that is:

- extendable: it should be easy to append information
- maintainable: it should remain easy to manipulate the content
- transparent: the methods for achieving different aspects should be clear
- able to stand alone: it does not require any special software or hardware to run
- scalable: it should be accessible from different platforms.

It is important to test each stage of development in its intended environment since variations in hardware — sizes and different resolutions of screens, varying processing speeds and varying graphics and sound capabilities — can bring about very different viewing experiences.

Step 7

Since the study guides were intended for distribution on the school Intranet, as well as on CD-ROM, html (including its recent incarnations such as dhtml and xml), was chosen as the underlying language of the study guide.

Macromedia Dreamweaver UltraDev was selected as a development environment because it offers an intuitive WYSIWYG (what you see is what you get) interface and, importantly, ready access to the underlying source code should the need arise, which is not true of all authoring tools. Allaire Homesite 4.0 was also used.

Evaluation

In a modern educational package, there are many different aspects to evaluate, including:

- ease of navigation
- effectiveness of communication
- learning outcomes
- general appeal
- costs *vs* benefits.

Evaluation of navigation should happen at an early stage. Where problems are identified, it is usual for the evaluation process to be iterated until a reasonable level of satisfaction is reached (*Step 8*).

Step 8

Recruiting volunteers for the small preliminary evaluation of the study guide interface proved a challenge. Initially, posters were placed in the school which invited students to view a template and offer feedback, and appealed to an interest in shaping their own education. Since there was no response to this campaign, first year students were addressed after the last lecture of the day (Wednesday lunchtime) and invited to a nearby room to view the CAL package on a laptop. This approach also failed to attract any volunteer evaluators, although it was stressed that the session would last no longer than ten minutes.

As a result, evaluation involves distributing the CAL study guide to fourth year students as they rotate through the department. Pre- and post-tests have been used to gauge baseline knowledge and subsequent changes. This methodology is subject to several confounding factors — CAL is notoriously difficult to evaluate and, where there is a traditional system already in use, evaluation becomes an ethical minefield. Qualitative data is being collected using pre- and post-questionnaires exploring attitudes to the package and to learning with computers in general. Logbooks are also used to identify patterns of use. The evaluation, which is ongoing, is an iterative process, which continues to inform the early stages of development.

Maintenance

When distributing knowledge that is rapidly changing, it is good practice to include a publishing date and a best before date. This is especially important in the case of CD-ROMs, where control over the information and its use is lost as soon as it passes from developer to user.

Since user feedback should be encouraged, full contact details for maintenance should be included.

All information on the master copy of the package must remain current, complete and accurate, and changes should be logged. With access to the Internet and e-mail, this burden can be considerably lightened with:

- e-mail alerts of current tables of contents from relevant publications
- electronic discussion lists or newsgroups
- logged literature searches.

Contact details of CD-ROM users should be kept so that updates can be communicated. An address of a website where bulletins and alerts can be posted should be included on the CD-ROM.

Conclusions

The development of a CAL package is a continuous, iterative process drawing on several disciplines. Success requires close attention to the needs of target group users, a dynamic approach which can anticipate and accommodate change, and stakeholder involvement at each stage. Although, evaluation and distribution of the final product are to come, there are early indications that applying this formula to this CD-ROM project will result in a versatile and well-received contribution to the spectrum of media at a learner's disposal.

CD-ROM project advisory panel:

Professor Gerry Bennett (Barts and the London, Academic Department of Older People)
Dr Richard Bull (Homerton Hospital, Consultant Dermatologist)

Dr John Davies (Queen Mary College, Research Support and Business Office)

Dr Patrick Gompertz (Geriatric Office)

Professor Sheila Hillier (Queen Mary College, Head of Division, Community Sciences)

Ms Alison Hopkins (Royal London Hospital, Mile End, Clinical Nurse Specialist)

Ms Valerie Joliffe (Bamboo Investments Plc)

Professor Robert Stout (Queen's University Belfast, Department of Geriatric Medicine)

Dr Diana Wood (Endocrinologist and Senior Lecturer in Outpatient Medicine, Royal London Hospital, Whitechapel)

Key points

- ❅ There is a healthy climate to support computer-assisted learning in the home and in institutions.

- ❅ A need for computer-assisted learning should be established before beginning the project.

- ❅ A number of authoring tools are available to facilitate in-house production by developers with a working knowledge of computers.

- ❅ Stakeholders should be involved at all stages of development.

- ❅ Knowledge should be validated and structured by experts.

- ❅ An infrastructure should be developed to maintain the knowledge and alert users to changes.

References

Abeles TP (1999) The academy in a wired world. In: Thorne M, ed. *Universities in the Future*. DTI, London

Cast (2000) Bobby Worldwide. Available at: http://www.cast.org/bobby/ accessed 12 March 2002

Coles C (1998) How students learn: the process of learning. In: Jolley B, Rees L, eds. *Medical Education in the Millennium*. OUP, Oxford: 63–82

Dix A, Finlay J, Abowd G, Beale R (1993) *Human Computer Interaction*. 2nd edn. Prentice Hall, London

Greenhalgh T (2001) Computer assisted learning in undergraduate medical education. *Br Med J* **322**: 40–4

Icon Bazaar (2001) Available at: http://www.Iconbazaar.com/computer/ accessed 23 January 2001

IT for All (1999) *Is IT for All?* DTI, London

Lusted HS, Knapp RB (1996) Controlling computers with neural signals. *Sci Am* **275**(4): 82–7

Mattheos N, Nattestad A, Attstrom R (2000) Local CD-ROM in interaction with HTML documents over the Internet. *Eur J Dent Educ* **4**: 124–7

Pennsylvania's Initiative on Assistive Technology (2001) WAVE 2.01. Available at: http://www.temple.edu/inst_disabilities/piat/wave/ accessed 12 March 2002

Preece J, Rogers Y, Benyon D *et al* (1994) *Human-computer Interaction*. Addison Wesley, Harlow

12

Curriculum vitae writing

Sheila McKenzie

Your CV is your passport to an interview, promotion and salary change. For a consultant post, the content and presentation make a huge impression, whether for an appointment, for discretionary points or for academic promotion. Under-representing your achievements is considered really bad form, because it could be interpreted that you assume everyone knows you or should know you and your achievements. If you cannot be bothered to explain your achievements in simple language for non-specialists then you will not impress. For many junior posts the competition is fierce. Those responsible for the short-listing have only your CV to go on. The days of either you or your old boss making a phone call to secure an appointment are long past. Proper presentation of yourself is everything.

General Rules

Front page

CVs should be fresh every time you apply for a post. The name of the post for which you are applying should be marked clearly on the front sheet, together with your name, degrees and the date.

Old and recycled CVs that omit current details will be spotted immediately. You should always use clean good quality paper. Faxes are not acceptable. If you are applying for a senior house officer (SHO) post, a folder is not necessary (it slows up the short-listing procedure) but a folder is a good idea for a consultant post. Forms, available online, are required for specialist registrar (SpR) posts with national training numbers. Make sure you follow to the letter all the instructions.

Font

Choice of font is important. The easiest text to read is serif which is a text with small tails which allows the eye to take in whole words at a time. Fancy fonts, italics, capital letters and central positioning all make reading difficult. Positioning is best as ragged right. Underlining is a leftover from the age of the typewriter and has been replaced by emboldening.

Personal details

The usual details may be followed by the name of your school. It's up to you! If you are applying for an SHO post you can mention your exam results.

At all levels it is important to mention abilities that show you are a good team player. Of all the professions, health care is the one where good working relationships are crucial to good outcomes, no matter how skilful you are. Travel abroad, what you learnt and how it would be useful to you in your chosen specialty, charity work, sporting achievements and all prizes and accolades should be mentioned. You must blow your own trumpet!

Previous training and experience

List your posts briefly. Don't worry about the size of the hospital or the number of beds. What people want to know is whether you have been properly supervised and trained to the level required for entry to the next level. At SHO level some of the best posts want their trainees fresh, as the employers feel they can train people properly from the start. So don't worry if you have not had any previous experience in the specialty. Find out what is expected before you apply.

For an SpR post you will have to enumerate the **medical skills** your college expects you to have learnt at this stage in your training. It is wise to obtain a copy of the application form so you know what is expected of you as soon as you know what specialty you want to enter. For all junior doctors there are College Curricula and, for most, Training Portfolios. You can say, 'I have been trained in the following procedures and skills as listed in the college Curriculum. I am applying for this post to extend my training in… (all the things you still need to learn)'. It will make a good impression if you say you have a training portfolio, especially one which includes reflective notes! You may be asked to produce this at interview.

The most difficult part of a CV for appointment at any level is to write the section on **communication skills**, to show you know how to deal with angry patients and relatives and so on. The best way to do this is to give examples. Most complaints result from poor communication. Your future employer will want to know that you are aware of this, have been trained in communication and are non-confrontational. If you are going for a junior post, you could give examples. 'During my post at so-and-so I was required to spend half an hour each day talking to a patient with a chronic disease (say cancer, chronic lung disease). From this I learnt....'. Or, 'I led the psychosocial meetings with the rehabilitation team. From this I learnt...'.

Demonstration of an understanding of what goes on in the community, such as visiting patients' homes, for example, to see how they get on after surgery, will make a huge impression. All of this is very individual and is one of the most revealing parts of a CV. You will be asked about holistic care and multi-disciplinary working at your interview, so make sure you outline your training in these areas in your CV.

Clinical **governance** and **audit** are important even for the most junior doctor. Make sure you have read the many guidelines on these issues and can explain what the importance of each is. ' I am familiar with... (the following publications)'. Make sure that you know about complaints procedures. You may have to write an essay about an audit project you have taken part in. If you have not completed a project, you can tactfully mention that 80% of junior doctors' audit is not completed and mention other governance endeavours that you have been involved with, such as case note review and critical incident review.

'Reflection' and '**reflective notes**' are now prominent in adult education. You could be asked to write an essay about a patient's management which changed your view about practice, or a case which demonstrated your communication skills. These essays are supposed to reveal how reflective you are. Reflective notes are accepted in CME. If you keep them, mention this in your CV.

How do you see **the future** in your chosen specialty? What are the biggest **challenges**? Remember, the future of health care for most people in the world is quite different from that in the West. Start with the future in developing countries. Don't be afraid to mention the relationship of health with war and politics, the effect of nutrition, infection, limb loss, blindness, and the relationship with education. Show that you have had a rounded education and can see further than the end of a microscope — or a scalpel. Mention the challenges of an ageing population, the cost of chronic illness, the increasing expectations of the public.

There is usually a section for **extras**. Give prominence to things that you've done related to healthcare delivery rather than personal achievements. These should also appear but as secondary.

The consultant CV

Applying for a first consultant post is a whole strategy. Is this the right job? If it isn't you'll soon be found out at interview if not before. Before starting on refining your CV find out what sort of person they want. Most trusts want a decent, personable competent colleague, not necessarily someone who will set the world on fire. At the same time, you will be expected to be keen on 'developing' and 'innovating' and 'complementing'. Your CV should reflect what is being asked for in the job description.

Personal details: A lot of applicants agonise over these because they feel that their nationality, religion, or marital status could go against them. A married woman, aged thirty-four, no children may feel that prospective employers will say to themselves, 'As soon as she gets a job she's going to start a family'. It's up to you how much you tell about yourself. It is helpful to list your defence union number and your GMC number.

Training: There is no need to go through every post ever undertaken and describe what you did. Simply emphasise what you have been trained in and what you can offer the new post. If you are going to work in a District General Hospital then the details of your MD are less important than details about training in management and governance.

Make sure you have read the NHS Plan, or whatever is the latest Department of Health strategy, and that you are familiar with the Primary Care Trust set up in the district you are going to. Stress, by giving examples in relation to your specialty, your training in leadership and the skills in which you are proficient, your training in multidisciplinary working, and your understanding of resource management. Stress your understanding of the balance between efficacy and cost, with some examples of how you see yourself working. In your interview, you are bound to be asked about things with which you don't agree. Ensure you know how to answer such questions diplomatically. 'What do you think of the Nurse Practitioner?' Don't say, 'They're all very well but...'. Everything before the 'but' is a lie! Don't say, 'Well, you have to be very careful'. Be as enthusiastic as you honestly can about everything that's new. 'Challenging' and 'exciting' are good words to practise. Pre-empt the questions by mentioning new ideas in your CV. Some trusts will invite short-listed candidates to make a presentation. Consider, at the time you are writing your CV, what, if asked, you might be expected to talk about. Then make sure you allude to this in your section on why you are applying for the post.

Know what you are entitled to. New consultants should have an office of their own and a secretary with equivalent sessions.

Courses, projects and research

Try to promote projects which have displayed your initiative. A CV which lists courses attended is very passive. Say why you attended them. The list should be balanced with projects and changes which you initiated afterwards. You can consult your reflective notes to remind you! Even if you only assisted in a research project you will have learnt something, such as the importance of a clear protocol, ethics approval and so on. If you have an impressive research record and are applying for a DGH post, emphasise how time spent in out-of-programme research has had side-benefits, such as prioritising, critical appraisal of perceived wisdom, presentation.

Take care with your publication list. Make sure you list original papers in peer reviewed journals separately from invited articles and letters. If you were a middle author, you might like to say what role you played. Embolden your own name.

Career aims for all posts

This the most important section at any level. First, your commitment to the specialty should be reflected here if you are a trainee. And, by the way, it is not enough to say, 'I am committed to becoming an orthopaedic surgeon'! Go on to mention why you have chosen the specialty and what excites you about it. If you are applying for a consultant post, your commitment to the area and the post should be convincing. Your prospective colleagues will want to know that you are making an active choice in wanting to join them. You should demonstrate good reasons for applying. A lot of homework needs to be done, including trying to see senior members of all the subspecialties which will be important to you. Second, it should be clear that you believe the post is going to give you some satisfaction and you see it as more than a paid job of work. Once again, 'challenge' is a good word. Third, mention complementary working. It is surprising how many consultants feel threatened by a new young energetic colleague who will undoubtedly have skills which they do not possess. Be alert to this. In your efforts to impress, make sure you don't make prospective colleagues feel inferior and out-of-date. Fourth, mention realistic developments you would like to undertake. So that they are realistic, you should have discussed anything that is likely to be expensive (and need a cost-benefit analysis) with the appropriate people beforehand. Finally, for all new posts you must be committed to good links with the community.

Other tips

Be patient with personnel departments, especially if they ask you for large numbers of copies of your CV. They don't have the time for photocopying and if you want the job you'll get on with it. An angry exchange with a recruitment officer, without question, will be related to those you would least want it to. You do not want to fail even before you have been sent the form.

For forms which have to be filled in online, make sure you don't leave any boxes empty. Use the font they have asked for. You will have to spend a lot of time summarising your achievements in order to fit the boxes. This can take many hours. It is obvious when applicants have taken the time to write clearly so that the CV can be easily read.

All those applying for a post for the first time should let as many peers and supervisors see the CV and take senior mentors' advice. The CV for any post, but particularly a first consultant post, will have to be revised many times. Start early, as soon as you know the post is available.

13

How to publish the findings of research

Huw TO Davies

Providing an account of research involves telling a story during which four key questions are answered: why did you start, what did you do, what did you find out and what does it mean? It is the third of these — what did you find out — that is at the heart of any research paper. Ensuring that the key messages emerge from the data is the duty of the author and requires considerable skill and craft.

Introduction

With many hundreds of journals now in circulation and tens of thousands of research papers published each year, consumers of medical knowledge need all the help that they can get. The clear presentation of research findings improves communication of key messages and aids the digestion of new medical knowledge. This chapter aims to guide those who wish to explain the findings from research studies in print. In doing so, it focuses largely on the presentation of data from quantitative research methodologies. Although many of the key messages are similar for the presentation of qualitative research findings, there are also additional difficulties which are not covered here — see Dey (1993), Silverman (2000) and Powell and Davies (2001).

Before beginning to communicate research findings on paper, it is worth asking oneself two questions:

- can I state in a single sentence the key message of my proposed paper?
- can I summarise in a few words why the research findings matter?

The discipline of trying to answer these questions with plausible, succinct and even elegant answers can do much to refine and focus what needs to be presented. A major difficulty in writing up any piece of research lies not in deciding what to say but in deciding what to leave out (Crombie and Davies, 1996).

Things in the right place

What follows focuses mainly on the presentation of research findings. This task is greatly eased, however, if the overall structure of a research article is well planned, with clearly delineated sections. Traditionally, research papers have followed the IMRaD format: introduction, methods, results and discussion. These sections answer, in turn, the four key questions asked of any research project (Crombie and Davies, 1996):

- why did you start?
- what did you do?
- what did you find out?
- what does it mean?

Making sure that the right information is included in each of these sections and appreciating that each has a separate function to perform helps ensure a crisp and coherent presentation of the key research findings.

Introduction

The introduction, obviously enough, introduces the area of study by identifying why it has importance, the state of current knowledge and the presence of any important gaps in that knowledge. Finishing off the introduction with a clear statement of the main research question helps prepare the reader for the findings — it sets an expectation of what will be presented as well as emphasising why it matters.

Methods

The methods section usually begins with a brief statement of the overall research design, eg. retrospective or prospective; experimental or observational; case report, survey, cohort, case-control or trial. This section should then describe the source of study subjects, the nature of their recruitment, the data collected and the means of analysing them. Clear expositions at this point mean that the flow of findings in the results section does not need to be interrupted by further explanations about how data were gathered and processed. Crucially, data should not be introduced at this point.

Results

The purpose of the results section is to provide an account of the findings from the research. Like all good accounts, it should have a logical structure and should be selective in what is covered. These issues will be explored in more detail later on. Significantly, the results section should not require any additional explication about data sources, processing or analysis, and nor should it stray into issues of meaning or inference — these are best left to the discussion section.

Discussion

This section often starts with a brief recap of the key findings (that one sentence statement prepared earlier, perhaps) and begins to outline their meaning and significance. It is here that the results are placed in the context of other published research (either confirming or contrasting), and it is in this section that the authors develop a critique of their own methods and data. Understanding the role and content of the discussion can assist in keeping extraneous material out of the results section.

Thus, a clear and coherent presentation of research findings is greatly aided by:

❖ A clear and focused research question, plainly presented in the introduction.
❖ A logical and precise explanation of data sources, processing and analysis (in the methods section), which sets a framework for the explication of the findings.
❖ A well-structured discussion, which gathers interpretation and critique properly separated from the data presentation.

Structuring the presentation of data

The presentation of research findings should be done in such a way that the reader is guided through what will often be a dense maze of data. From these data, information must be extracted which will then be placed in context and interpreted for meaning in the discussion. Thus, all data are not equal in the eyes of the reader, and it is the job of the author to construct a path through the data maze in such a way that the story of interest can emerge. The first task is to develop a structure for introducing data and analyses.

Quantitative research in biomedicine almost always involves study subjects of one sort or another. Often these will be patients; sometimes they will be other individuals, such as members of the public or staff. In either case, a good beginning for any results section is some descriptive data on the individuals and their characteristics. From this simple beginning, data pertaining to the key research questions can begin to be introduced. In doing so, it is better to have some logical rationale underlying the sequence of introduction: sometimes this will be suggested by the way in which research questions are cast; at other times the logic will have been laid out in the methods section.

Often the research design itself imposes a discipline on what data should be presented and in which order, eg. with a survey one would expect some initial data to allow an assessment of the representativeness of the sample; with a trial the initial analysis should compare the two groups at baseline. Whatever, the rationale should be explicit, and it should be consistent between the different sections of the paper. Further, it is better to start with simpler analyses, eg. a univariate approach, and gradually develop more complex ideas, eg. multivariate analyses.

Describing data

The results section of most research papers consists of two key elements:

- the presentation of data in tables and figures
- the accompanying prose narrative.

It is a mistake to think either that these should duplicate each other or that they should simply cover complementary parts of the analysis. In truth, they serve different functions, and ideally each element should more or less be capable of comprehensible consultation in isolation.

The tables and figures should provide a comprehensive view of the data. By using short but informative titles and legends, it should be possible for a reader to understand the nature of the analysis and the key findings simply by consulting the tables and figures in sequence. In complementary fashion, the accompanying narrative should guide the reader through the tables/figures, highlighting their salient features and drawing attention to the threads of the arguments that make the findings interesting. Thus, while the narrative will contain many references to the tables and figures, such references do not stand instead of providing an account — they refer to the tables and figures as supporting evidence for the arguments explicated.

Data presentation

Data in tables need to be presented using measures of average (mean, median or mode) and spread (range, interquartile range or standard deviation). Different data require different presentation and the mean ± standard deviation may not always be appropriate (Davies 1998a, b). Tables themselves should be constructed with a minimum of horizontal ruling and no vertical rules. All column headings and row identifiers should be readily intelligible; table items should be presented in both absolute (number) and relative (eg. percentage) form. The use of row and/or column subtotals may also be helpful. The intention is to provide a complete picture, fit for the purpose, without overloading the reader with extraneous detail.

Inferential statistics should be used sparingly, consistent with the research questions that are being posed. Current usage of statistics in medicine is now beginning to favour the presentation of confidence intervals over hypothesis testing with P values

(Gardner and Altman, 1986; Davies, 1998c; Sterne and Davey-Smith, 2001). In either case, however, the analysis strategy, with prior reasons for selected comparisons, needs to be explained in advance to avoid accusations of fishing or data dredging. A common error is to present data with insufficient information for their interpretation. For example, numbers alone are often uninterpretable — they may have to be expressed as some sort of rate or ratio to make them so. Likewise, numbers that do not take into account chance variability are unsatisfactory.

Aiding critical appraisal

The development of critical appraisal (Davies, 2000) as part of evidence-based medicine has highlighted the sorts of information that should be covered in the presentation of research. A good discipline then is to apply critical appraisal skills to any paper under development. The existence of numerous checklists for specific study designs can greatly help this process (see Crombie, 1996; Greenhalgh, 1997; Sackett *et al*, 1997), and further guidance can also be found in the users' guides developed by the Evidence-based Medicine Working Group, which are available on the Internet (http://www.cche.net/).

The intention in using critical appraisal during the authoring process is to identify whether sufficient data and detail are provided to allow any reader to assess both the internal and the external validity of the findings. This approach can help highlight any unfortunate confusion or omissions.

Conclusion

The primary purpose of research papers is to communicate worthwhile messages in such a way that they are open to critical scrutiny. Good data do not necessarily speak for themselves. Clearly written and well-presented research findings can greatly aid the easy interpretation of important new data.

In presenting new data, the author(s) need to act as 'expert guides' through complex terrain. This requires considerable skills in selecting, structuring and explaining: it is insufficient simply to 'dump' all the data into tables and to force the reader to find their own way through. Further, reflective reading of drafts in the light of critical appraisal checklists can also help produce more robust and intelligible accounts of research. Such improvements in the presentation of research findings not only assist readers but also increase the likelihood of publication in the first place.

Key points

✳ Coherent presentation of research findings begins with a crisp explanation of the main research question(s). It is then the author's task to tell the story of how this question was addressed.

✳ Clarity in presentation is greatly aided by a clear separation of material between the different sections of the paper: introduction, methods, results and discussion.

✳ The role of the results section is to guide the reader through the data, highlighting the key features of interest.

✳ The tables and the prose in the results section should each provide an account of the data, separately intelligible yet nonetheless complementary.

✳ Data presentation should begin with basic descriptions of study subjects and simpler analyses before going into greater detail.

✳ The structural logic and the choice of content in the results section can be guided by an awareness of what should be included to facilitate critical appraisal of the research.

References

Crombie IK (1996) *The Pocket Guide to Critical Appraisal*. BMJ Publishing Ltd, London

Crombie IK, Davies HTO (1996) *Research in Health Care: Design Conduct and Interpretation of Health Services Research*. John Wiley & Sons, Chichester

Davies HTO (1998a) Informative presentation of summary data. *Hosp Med* **59**: 154–5

Davies HTO (1998b) Describing and estimating: use and abuse of standard deviation and standard error. *Hosp Med* **59**: 327–8

Davies HTO (1998c) Assessing chance variability in treatment trials. *Hosp Med* **59**: 650–2

Davies HTO (2000) Introducing critical appraisal. *Hosp Med* **61**: 432–3

Dey I (1993) *Qualitative Data Analysis. A User Friendly Guide for Social Scientists*. Routledge, London

Gardner MJ, Altman DG (1986) Confidence intervals rather than *P* values: estimation rather than hypothesis testing. *Br Med J* **292**: 746–50

Greenhalgh T (1997) *How to Read a Paper: The Basics of Evidence-based Medicine*. BMJ Publishing Group, London

Powell AE, Davies HTO (2001) Reading and assessing qualitative research. *Hosp Med* **62**: 360–3

Sackett DL, Richardson WS, Rosenberg W, Haynes RB (1997) *Evidence-based Medicine: How to Practice and Teach EBM*. Churchill Livingstone, London

Silverman D (2000) *Doing Qualitative Research. A Practical Handbook*. Sage Publications, London

Sterne JAC, Davey-Smith G (2001) Sifting the evidence — what's wrong with significance tests? *Br Med J* **322**: 226–31

14

Publishing on the Internet: why bother?

Geoffrey Nuttall

This chapter outlines the rationale for the author who is thinking of publishing material directly via the Internet rather than through the established channels of publishing houses and peer-reviewed journals.

Publishing 'sans frontières'?

Getting published on the Internet can be virtually cost free, instantaneous, universal in its distribution and unfettered in its quality control, and there is no shortage of medical authors willing to participate in this.

However, as attractive as it may seem, publishing 'sans frontières' is manifested in the very problem of information overload, which Kiley has already described in *Chapter 1* (Kiley, 2000) and of which every critical user of the Internet must be painfully aware. Therefore, despite its superficial attractions of speed, low cost and universality, the lack of quality control should caution the author to think carefully before deciding to publish directly on the Internet and to ask themselves the question, 'What is the point?' At present, the answer is probably, 'Not much'.

E-books

For the author seeking to make a commercial success of Internet publishing, Stephen King's experience with the online serial publication of *The Plant* should serve as a salutary lesson (http//www.stephenking.com).[1]

While the Internet does allow authors to become, in effect, their own publishing house, the failure of *The Plant* illustrates that the majority of people still prefer to read words on paper rather than on screen and that there is still a reluctance to pay for online material. This may change, but to date nearly all medical e-books are in fact electronic versions of paper books, and while they do generate extra sales, they would not be financially viable if only available in electronic format, despite doing away with the costs of paper and distribution.

Publishing articles online

For the author seeking to further their career through publishing academic material on the Internet, the need for caution is even greater. Indeed, there is some merit in the argument that the Internet *per se* is a medium only to be approached with extreme scepticism.

One of the reasons for this was vividly illustrated in an article in *Cancer* (Biermann *et al*, 1999). Here, the authors conducted a comprehensive search of the information available online for Ewing's sarcoma. They took factors such as the search

---

1   King released the book chapter by chapter exclusively on the Internet and readers were asked to subscribe. Relative to the sales which would have been generated by conventionally publishing the book it was a commercial failure and folded before the completion of the online publication.

engine used, terms used to search, the type of information source, whether the publication was peer reviewed and so forth into account. They found that the stated survival rate on the Internet for Ewing's sarcoma varied in the search results from 5% to 85%. Consequently, information, and its authorship, published on the Internet can only be properly valued if it has been subject to quality control before, or soon after, publication.

At the moment, formal quality control on the Internet remains principally a function of peer-reviewed journals which have opted to publish online. However, new initiatives to address the issue of quality control effectively, but also to implement and streamline the 'traditional' system of peer review online, are currently being sought, and, if successful, they will make the decision whether or not to publish on the Internet more attractive and more academically sound.

New initiatives

Of these new initiatives, at least two deserve serious consideration, because they seem to offer the author all the advantages of rapid publication and access to peer review without the delays and frustrations so often accompanying publication in traditional print-on-paper journals.

Clinical Medicine and Health Research NetPrints

The first, Clinical Medicine and Health Research NetPrints (Clinmed) (http://clinmed.netprints.org), is the result of a collaboration between the BMJ Publishing Group and Stanford University Libraries (Delamothe *et al*, 1999).

Authors can submit articles 'before, during, or after peer

review by other agencies' (Delamothe *et al*, 1999), which, after screening for confidentiality and libel, are posted on the Clinmed server where they can be updated by the authors as often as they wish and viewed and commented on by peers. This does not constitute proper peer review, but authors hopefully benefit from the feedback. If they wish to do so, authors can forward their papers to 'any peer-reviewed journal that will accept submissions that have appeared as electronic preprints' (Delamothe *et al*, 1999). An extensive list of journals that do so is available on the website, including, for example, the *British Medical Journal*, *The Lancet* and *Cancer*.

However, Clinmed also accommodates electronic reprints as well as preprints — after publication in a peer-reviewed journal, authors can archive their articles on the site, providing that they have retained the right to do so.

It is just over two years since Clinmed was launched, and it is still too early to say how successful it will ultimately become. Nevertheless, with its aim to 'allow researchers to share their findings in full, for free, and as soon as their studies are complete' (Delamothe *et al*, 1999), it seems to be a viable, new and alternative way for the dissemination of information and stimulation of feedback and debate and potentially a valuable staging post, depending on the feedback received, on the way to publication in a peer-reviewed journal.

What criticism there is of it centres principally around the fact that it is not linked to the ever more dominant citation indices, so new work posted on it will not attract a critical mass of peers willing to advise and interact with each other unless the idea and principles of preprints become more popular in the biomedical field. Those for whom the time delay of traditional peer review is a problem may feel that this process will introduce a further delay, although this site is intended to augment peer review rather than replace it.

A note of caution: when considering whether to post material on a preprint server, it should be borne in mind that some of the most prestigious journals, such as the *New England Journal of Medicine*, will not consider articles for publication which have been previously published as preprints.

BioMed Central

Another new initiative is BioMed Central (http://www.biomedcentral.com), which differs from Clinmed in that the material electronically submitted by authors is peer reviewed by the extensive editorial board of BioMed Central and then published in one of its over fifty publications. Whereas Clinmed might be seen as a potentially huge medical archive with feedback facilities, BioMed Central 'is an independent publishing house committed to providing immediate free access to peer-reviewed biomedical research'.

BioMed Central is attractive because it is linked to PubMed Central, and thus accepted articles are available to a wide audience through the National Institutes of Health's (NIH) PubMed database, although this does not mean that the author's work is recognised by the NIH's Index Medicus; journals are included in PubMed through links rather than being assessed and accepted by a review body, and inclusion in PubMed does not therefore confer citation in itself.

Authors who publish their papers in one of BioMed Central's journals retain copyright of their work. However, 'authors agree to allow free and unrestricted non-commercial use of the work by others. They also grant to BioMed Central an exclusive license to commercial redistribution and use of the published article' and to 'identify itself as the original publisher'.

BioMed Central is a commercial site whose future sustainability depends on its ability to exploit its content commercially through advertising and the sale of subsidiary rights; requirements that are no different from the establishment journal publishing model. Additionally, it is questionable whether any one organisation can really provide a peer review team sufficiently large and committed to be capable of offering advice on a par with the extensive resources of the major specialised journals. Note: from 1 January, 2002, Biomed Central levy an article processing charge of $500 per article accepted for publication. Waivers may be granted, particularly for authors from developing countries.

Online submission to established journals

If question marks remain over the long-term future of specific Internet initiatives, the author still has the option of submitting articles to established journals that are also published on the Internet, although many journals surprisingly do not seem to encourage online submission, eg. *The Lancet*.

Others, like the *British Journal of Anaesthesia*, in seeking to adapt to the perceived opportunities and threats of the Internet, have adopted experimental strategies which a prospective author should take into consideration (Smith, 2001). In the case of the *British Journal of Anaesthesia*, while retaining the print-on-paper version, a concise version was produced at the start of 2001, containing the abstracts, with the full text of articles appearing online. While typesetting, printing and dispatch costs were reduced as a result, the accessibility of the articles to the readership was drastically restricted by being readable only on screen, and because the online publication was still linked to the dispatch cycle of the print-on-paper version, the possible advantage of rapid publication was not available to authors any more than in a purely print-on-paper journal. The experiment ceased after six months, and was possibly ahead of its time.

Conclusion

The idealised vision of the Internet, liberating authors from the constraints of the traditional peer-review process created by the editorial boards and the vested interests of the established publishers, is still far from being realised, and is probably naïve.

It should also be remembered that some organisations which most vociferously support the new order are themselves dependent for their commercial survival on the maintenance of the status quo, either because they themselves are traditional journal publishers or because the Internet provides opportunities for creating new monopolies of peer review and the subsequent commercial exploitation of authors' material. Consequently, in deciding where to publish, authors should look at the fundamentals and not, like many investors in dot.coms, be seduced by 'new' media and its entrepreneurs.

Key points

* The Internet makes self-publishing quick, easy and low cost.

* The Internet allows publication without quality control.

* Stand alone e-books have yet to prove themselves commercially.

* Internet alternatives to established journals are unproven.

* Traditional models of peer review still dominate.

* An author should apply the same critical standards to online as to traditional publishing.

References

Biermann JS, Golladay GJ, Greenfield MLVH, Baker LH (1999) Evaluation of cancer information on the Internet. *Cancer* **86**: 1875–9

Delamothe T, Smith R, Keller MA, Sack J, Witscher B (1999) Netprints: the next phase in the evolution of biomedical publishing. *Br Med J* **319**: 1515–6

Kiley R (2000) Finding health information on the Internet: health professionals. *Hosp Med* **61**: 736–8

Smith G (2001) Editorial II, Publishing changes in 2001. *Br J Anaesth* **86**(1): 3–4

15

How to write a review article

Robin CN Williamson

Writing a good review article is a real challenge. It requires not just a detailed literature search but a thorough 'digest' of the material obtained. Readers seek an up-to-date guide through a morass of data that has been sifted by the author and then integrated into a coherent and authoritative account.

A popular format

I used to have a close involvement with a surgical journal that conducted regular surveys of its readership. The editors would invite comments on the type of article included and the appropriate balance between original material and expert review. 'More review articles please' was a consistent refrain. Authors like review articles because they help to establish their own status as experts in the field. Editors like them because they are good for the citation index. Readers like them because they provide a short cut to the acquisition of knowledge.

Journals tend to be more readily available than textbooks, especially if they are published online. Moreover, the information they contain is usually more up-to-date, given the gestation time of most books (other than conference proceedings). Review articles are especially popular with those researching in the same field or those required to lecture on the topic. They help to assuage the constant fear that crucial new facts have been overlooked. An author or lecturer may be dull or verbose, but he/she hates to be considered out of touch.

Before considering the genesis of a review article, it may help to regard their place in the overall scheme of medical writing. Although the balance varies widely from one medical journal to another, most published articles can be classified into one of six different categories, as follows:

1. Leading articles or editorials, which are generally commissioned by the editor. They should be short and authoritative statements that highlight a topical subject. Sometimes the editorial arises from a paper that is published in the same issue of the journal, in which case it should aim to set these new data in context with previous related work.

2. Review articles, which are generally unsolicited and which set out to cover the field in much greater depth than an editorial. It follows that a review article should be much more heavily referenced: it is the main course not the starter.

3. Original articles, which present new clinical or laboratory studies. Each original article will try to relate the new findings to the old, but it is the task of a review article to take an objective and comprehensive look at the whole field. (See also *Chapter 13*.)

4. Case reports, which should briefly present one or two patients of exceptional interest. Beware the format 'case report and review of the literature'. A detailed review is seldom justified on the basis of such slender experience. Three or more examples of a rare condition might represent a small series that is worth discussing at slightly greater length, but for a simple case report you should keep the references to a bare minimum (as often dictated by the instructions to authors). (See also *Chapter 3*.)

5. Debates: some journals choose to highlight a controversial

topic not with an editorial or review article that weighs up the arguments and reaches an interim verdict itself, but with a pair of articles that present alternative views and allow readers to make up their own minds. The 'debate' format may also be used to advance a new hypothesis or publicise a piece of lateral thinking.

6. Letters to the editor, which allow the percipient reader to correct a point that has been missed by the referees and the editorial board (see *Chapter 10*) or to draw attention to a relevant personal contribution.

Thus, a review article differs from an editorial primarily in the extent of its coverage, but partly also in the requirement for topicality. A good review article is valuable even if it covers a well-established field, although a wise author will still wish to draw particular attention to innovative contributions.

The authors' credentials

The urge to publish a review article might follow a set of clinical or experimental studies centred on a common theme or a detailed literature search undertaken to write up a retrospective case series. You may feel that it is a pity to waste all the knowledge gained from this exercise. Perhaps the field is one that is expanding fast or is relatively under-reported.

The potential author of a review article has often conducted a period of formal research towards a higher degree. You will then have concentrated upon the subject for a couple of years and will have digested a large number of papers for the 'background' to a thesis, thereby becoming a world expert on what may be quite a narrow area. These are appropriate credentials for attempting to write a review article, provided that you can appreciate that a good review is a rather different entity from the historical background to a thesis. It is necessary to be more selective and more concise, but this need will be revisited below.

Some of the best review articles are written by experts who have worked in the field for many years and have learned to assess the weight of evidence in a particular area, but such experts may have insufficient time or interest to tackle the substantial amount of fresh work that is needed. They have probably covered the subject before in original articles, book chapters or previous review articles. A 'catch 22' situation can therefore arise. The new initiate has the time and interest to undertake a review, yet the journal editor may be uncertain of his/her track record and feel that he/she lacks the authority for the successful overview of a complex subject. Put simply, you may be anxious to make your name in the field but find it difficult to get your work published because no-one has heard of you.

One way to avoid this outcome is to ensure that you cite your own original research in the bibliography. If the review article is good enough, of course, then the problem is overcome by the self-evident maturity of its author. An alternative ploy is to have multiple authors, the first of these carrying out the literature search while the last and more senior gives the whole work his/her personal stamp. This formula often works very well in practice, but there are two caveats. First, in the context of a review article (or book chapter) multiple authors should mean only two or three, depending upon the spread of subject areas; a combination of basic scientist and clinician can be very effective in this regard.

Second, authorship of a review article implies a substantial contribution, as it should for any type of medical writing. It is not enough for the senior author just to put his/her name to the text after a cursory inspection of the initial draft. He/she should have been involved at the planning stage and should have played an active part in the content and style of the work. In this way, the authority of experience can be harnessed to the vigour of youth. I do not suppose that I am the only editor to have struggled through an article and wondered if the senior author had ever taken the trouble to read it before putting his/her name to such palpably inadequate work.

Preparation

Writing is a hard discipline and especially so in the case of a review article, in which the author has to decide where to begin and end and how much to include. Careful preparation can smooth the subsequent path. Before putting pen to paper or fingers to keyboard, the following preparatory steps should be considered:

1. It goes without saying that you must read widely on the subject before attempting a critical review. It takes time, effort and experience to assimilate the literature plus a degree of organisational skill. Resist the temptation to cite every single paper that you have read. Some writings can safely be discarded as irrelevant, while others will have been superseded by fresh work in the field. It is crucial to be up-to-date; nothing can scupper a review article as quickly as the discovery that the author has overlooked important new contributions. This risk can arise when you return to the field after an interval of a couple of years.

2. A comprehensive review article represents a considerable investment on the authors' part, and it is disappointing to have the work turned down because the journal has recently accepted a similar paper. Once you have done the initial assessment, therefore, it may be worth writing to the editor to say that you plan to submit a review article by a certain date and inviting his/her comments. Most editors are glad to receive good reviews, while being careful to avoid

guarantees of acceptance. They will surely let you know if any similar article is going through the editorial process or if they feel that your project is of limited interest to the readers. One snag of this policy arises if you set a submission date that lies too far ahead or that you are unable to keep. Medical knowledge moves on apace, and the editor may become bored of waiting.

3. Think carefully about the authorship. Your best friend may not be the most appropriate ally in this regard. Some of the best reviews integrate clinical work with basic science, and you may not necessarily have the expertise to cover both parts with equal authority. You stray beyond the bounds of experience at your peril. Clinicians are irritated by laboratory scientists who purport to understand patient care, and there is no doubt that the reverse holds true.

    If you decide to involve a senior colleague, be sure to elicit his/her active input from an early stage. I have known problems arise when a young doctor decides to continue in a field of research beyond the period of his/her thesis and wishes to leave the nest and fly by him/herself. His/her erstwhile supervisor may feel nettled about this show of independence and wish to be included as a co-author into the distant future. Whereas original work performed under guidance or supervision should never be published without permission, review articles are a grey area. With reasonable goodwill on both sides, the matter should be soluble by proper consultation. A wise supervisor should rejoice if he/she has launched another expert in the field and a tactful fledgling esteems the advice of his/her mentor.

4. Be sure to adopt the house style of your target journal. Time taken reading the instructions to authors is seldom time wasted. Courtesies count in the field of medical publishing. You should therefore adopt American spelling if you plan to submit (or resubmit) your work to a journal published in the

United States. You will get a feel for the layout and style of the journal if you read other reviews that have been published in recent issues.

The format

The writer of a review article has an immediate difficulty to overcome in organising the layout. There is no uniformly accepted convention that equates to the introduction, methods, results and discussion of an original article (see *Chapter 13*). Although some might regard it as a straitjacket, I have always found this standard arrangement both comforting and convenient (Williamson, 1996). With a review article, by contrast, the organisation of material is left to the author's own devices. It can even be difficult to concoct a meaningful abstract — assuming that this is a requirement of the journal — which avoids clichés such as 'the investigation and management are discussed'. On mature reflection, however, it should be possible to summarise the most important matters that you have discussed, akin to writing the key points of a chapter. Here, in particular, it is valuable to consult other reviews that have appeared in the same journal.

The introduction assumes considerable importance. One should set out clearly the objectives of the paper and describe the source material, eg. a literature search that starts with a previous review in, say, 1970. The use of subheadings is essential. Apart from breaking up acres of text, they clarify the scope of your work and allow a cursory reader to focus on a few areas of special interest.

A review article should not be a vehicle for presenting unpublished personal data, but it is appropriate to record one's own published contributions to the field. Nor is it a mathematical exercise such as a meta-analysis, in which statistical significance is sought from a series of related studies. There is room for tables that summarise published data or highlight conflicting work in the literature, but the cornerstone of a good review is a balanced text that guides the reader through the wealth of available material.

Case reports are not generally included, although it might be reasonable to present a short illustrative example. A limited number of figures can achieve the same effect in a more attractive fashion, provided that the legends give sufficient detail to the reader. At the end of the review, you should try to draw some overall conclusions and point to areas in which future work is needed.

A chief reason for the enduring popularity of review articles derives from an extensive bibliography, so care should be devoted to this section. Readers use a good review to gain a rapid entrée to the relevant literature. In gratitude, they are likely to cite your article when they write their own paper on some aspect of the subject. Please ensure that the references are correct; it is annoying to try and follow up a promising lead only to lose track of the crucial paper through inaccuracies in the volume number or year of issue listed. There is no magic number of references for a review, but in practice it will often exceed one hundred if the topic is of sufficient interest and the corpus of published work allows. The skill lies in making every reference count. One way to do this is to refer to other papers that have summarised certain aspects of the field in a useful manner. This ploy is especially helpful if you want to describe the early development of a subject without citing each and every historical reference.

The style

I have left this aspect to the last because it is so difficult to categorise what distinguishes an enjoyable and informative paper from a turgid account sure to deter all but the most avid seeker after knowledge. Doctors tend to be busy people who are unlikely to bother with a dreary treatise; they expect a review to be both succinct and comprehensive, both readable and logical.

The ideal review starts with a careful choice of material, describing important developments and setting out controversies, and it presents the whole in an attractive package. Above all, readers expect authoritative comment rather than annotated bibliography. You are the expert: it is not enough just to set out the facts for and against a particular theory; you are expected to interpret them on behalf of the reader. You have had the time to consider the evidence, so try to impart your own opinion without excessive slant one way or the other. The reader seeks an informed guide through the relevant literature and will accept a certain amount of partiality in your verdict if you present the crux of the argument. If not, then the editor is likely to publish the ensuing correspondence, which may give you another chance to express the reasons for your opinion.

A review article is different from the background section of a thesis, in which the author might reasonably wish to cite almost any work related to the field if only to demonstrate the breadth of his/her reading. It is more compressed and must therefore be selective. At first sight, writing a review might seem to be easier than writing an original paper, which requires the design and conduct of novel research. However, it can take almost as long to sift through the published work and provide a coherent account of a complex subject. Be prepared to seek advice and to pursue perfection through several drafts. Try to adopt a style that progresses logically from one paragraph to the next. Each paragraph is like a mini paper. It introduces a concept, tosses the arguments to and fro and concludes with a summary statement that leads logically to its successor. This maintains a constant thread and with it the reader's interest. A well-written review should be immensely satisfying to you as the author, and it is timeless in the sense that it encapsulates knowledge at a particular moment.

Key points

- ✼ Do not underestimate the amount of work required to provide a high-quality review article.

- ✼ Give careful thought to the need for suitable co-authors (if any).

- ✼ Embark on your literature search, then 'digest' the relevant papers.

- ✼ Aim to impart your personal stamp on the work you discuss. You are the expert, so the reader expects you to weigh up the evidence and reach a mature conclusion. Be succinct as well as authoritative.

- ✼ Remember that a good review article differs from the background section of a thesis by being more selective in its coverage.

- ✼ Give thought to the best layout since there is no uniform convention. Use subheadings and consider a little illustrative material.

- ✼ Introduce the scope of the article and then proceed in a logical succession of paragraphs towards a measured conclusion.

Reference

Williamson RCN (1996) Writing a surgical paper. *Ann Acad Med Singapore* **25**: 305–8